INTRODUCTION TO
MODERN MATHEMATICS

INTRODUCTION TO
MODERN MATHEMATICS

HERBERT MESCHKOWSKI

translated by
A. MARY TROPPER M.Sc. Ph.D.
Queen Mary College
University of London

GEORGE G. HARRAP & CO. LTD
LONDON · TORONTO · WELLINGTON · SYDNEY

Originally published in German under the title
Einführung in die moderne Mathematik
Hochschultaschenbücher 75

First published in Great Britain 1968
by GEORGE G. HARRAP & CO. LTD
182 High Holborn, London, W.C.1

© *Bibliographisches Institut AG, Mannheim* 1964
© *English translation George G. Harrap & Co. Ltd* 1968
Copyright. All rights reserved

245 59109 5

Composed in Monophoto Times and printed by
J. W. Arrowsmith Ltd., Winterstoke Rd., Bristol 3

Made in Great Britain

PREFACE

Some decades ago it was customary to begin the study of mathematics with an 'Introduction to higher mathematics'. By *higher mathematics* was chiefly meant infinitesimal calculus. University mathematics differed from school mathematics mainly in the exact treatment of limit problems. It was not easy for the beginner to become accustomed to the reasoning involved in 'epsilonology'. Hence there was the introduction whose main aim was to prepare for an understanding of the problems of infinitesimal calculus.

In the meantime work with limits found its way into the schools. Unfortunately even today such problems are still not always treated in schools with the desirable precision; but nevertheless sixth forms do provide a preparation which helps the transition to university lectures.

Today the difficulties of the beginner are, on the whole, of a different kind. For the universities, mathematics is the 'science of formal systems' and the approach to modern formalism often presents the sixth-former with considerable difficulties. Perhaps in a few decades the situation will be different, when the 'Bourbaki ideas' have found their way into schools. Today there appears to be a need to help the students in their first university terms with an 'introduction' which will facilitate the treatment of axioms, sets and logical symbols. Perhaps such a text may also be of interest to engineers and teachers, who finished their studies some time ago.

This 'introduction' begins with a chapter on axiomatics and then introduces the most important elementary structures. It concludes with a theory of real numbers. The treatment of *integers* given in Chapter III is an extension (not published so far) of a method due to Erhard Schmidt for operations with *natural numbers*.

Against the theory of real numbers given in the last chapter (which follows from the work of Hahn, Ellers, and Dzewas) one could object that the classical methods (nests of intervals, Dedekind section) are at least not more difficult than those presented here. We have decided to present the filter theory of real numbers, since it provides an exercise for manipulation with a concept which is important in topology.

The bibliography at the end of the book is meant to encourage further reading.

HERBERT MESCHKOWSKI
Berlin

TABLE OF CONTENTS

CHAPTER ONE

Axioms

1. Examples of proofs

If one wants to prove the well-known formula

$$(a+b)^2 = a^2 + 2a \cdot b + b^2 \tag{1}$$

for natural numbers a and b, one can proceed as follows: By the 'distributive law'

$$c \cdot (a+b) = c \cdot a + c \cdot b \tag{2}$$

and taking into account

$$a \cdot b = b \cdot a \tag{3}$$

we have

$$(a+b)^2 = (a+b) \cdot (a+b) = (a+b) \cdot a + (a+b) \cdot b$$
$$= a^2 + b \cdot a + a \cdot b + b^2 = a^2 + 2a \cdot b + b^2$$

But how do we know that the 'distributive law' (2) and the 'commutative law' (3) are correct? Can these formulae also be *proved*?

Some readers will be satisfied by referring to a numerical example. We have

$$3 \cdot 4 = 4 \cdot 3 = 12, \qquad 5 \cdot 6 = 6 \cdot 5 = 30$$

and it will not be possible to find two natural numbers a and b for which $a \cdot b = b \cdot a$ is false. The distributive law (2) can be made plausible when we recall the usual procedure for elementary numerical calculations. If we want to find 8 times 27, we *do* add 8 times 20 and 8 times 7.

$$8 \cdot 27 = 8 \cdot (20+7) = 8 \cdot 20 + 8 \cdot 7 = 160 + 56 = 216$$

But has this reference the force of a proof? Surely we have shown only that we *do* use the distributive law (2) for calculations, but this is not a *proof*.

We say of a mathematical theorem that it is *proved*, if it is justified by logical deductions from already known theorems. But this referring back to 'already known' theorems cannot be continued *ad infinitum*. For every mathematical theory we must have a foundation on which we can build, *i.e.*, a system of theorems which do not require proof, and which we shall make the basis of our theory. To decide this important question we shall first of all discuss briefly the ideas of mathematicians of past centuries.

2. Classical theory of proofs

Let us begin with an attempt to clarify the nature of the 'basic theorems' (usually called axioms). To do this we go back to Pascal's 'rules' (for definitions, axioms and proofs). The ingenious French mathematician (1623–62) recommends:[1]

Rules for definitions

1. Do not define objects, which in themselves are so well known that no clearer concepts exist for their definition.
2. Do not leave undefined any obscure and ambiguous concepts.
3. Use in the definition only words which are either perfectly known or have already been defined.

Rules for axioms

1. For every necessary principle, no matter how clear and evident it may be, ask first whether it will be accepted.
2. Choose as axioms only perfectly self-evident concepts.

Rules for proofs

1. Do not attempt to prove anything which is so self-evident that nothing clearer exists with which to prove it.
2. Prove all theorems which are not quite clear and use for their proof only very obvious axioms or already accepted or proved theorems.
3. Always replace in one's mind the defined term by the definition, lest one is deceived by the lack of precision in the concepts that have been made precise by the definition.

[1] Pascal: *Oeuvres Complètes*. Bibliothèque de la Pléiade, pp. 596, 597.

To the critical reader of these 'rules' several questions will suggest themselves. What is so self-evident that nothing clearer exists? May we consider the commutative law or, say, the equation $a = a$, as self-evident? And how far can one go with the defining? It is relatively simple to relate derived concepts in mathematics to 'elementary' ones. Thus one can, for example, define a triangle as a system of three points.[1] But what is a point? In Euclid we find the classical definition: *A point is that which has no parts.* One can admit that this definition uses words which are 'perfectly known' in the sense of Pascal. Nevertheless one can do very little with it. It really states only what a point is *not* (*i.e.*, that which has a part).

Many attempts have been made to give a better definition.[2] But all these attempts do not stand up to serious criticism and one is inclined to recall Pascal's first rule for definitions. Perhaps we have to be content that a point is *so well known in itself* that every definition becomes meaningless.

The statement that the basic concepts of mathematics are *known in themselves* may be understandable from Plato's theory of knowledge. The teachings of this great thinker about the nature of mathematics influenced the pronouncements of mathematicians and philosophers for more than two thousand years. When, for example, Ernst Goldbeck writes in 1924:

"In mathematics we have an immense realm of ideas, the breadth and depth of which nobody has yet grasped",

he shows himself as an adherent of the Platonian doctrine of ideas. For, according to Plato, knowledge of mathematics is *insight into the realm of ideas.* So he writes, for example, in *The Republic:*[3]

"You also know how they [mathematicians] make use of visible figures and discourse about them, though what they really have in mind is the originals of which these figures are images: they are not reasoning, for instance, about this particular square and diagonal which they have drawn, but about *the* Square and *the* Diagonal, and so in all cases. The diagrams they draw and the models they make are actual things, which may have their shadows or images in water; but now they serve in their turn as images, while the student is seeking to behold those realities which only thought can apprehend."

[1] One can also formulate the definition differently.
[2] See, for example, Meschkowski (1), p. 5.
[3] *The Republic of Plato*, Book VI, No. 510.

The relation between the perceptual objects and the (for Plato very real) 'ideas' can best be made clear by the famous allegory of the cave. The man chained to the cave wall can see only the shadow pictures of things which the fire throws on the wall. Occupation with mathematics, however, requires a turning away of one's glance from the shadow to the things themselves. The mathematician is concerned with the *concept* of a circle, with the *concept* of a straight line and not with the pictures of these concepts created by man's hand on the blackboard or on paper. These concepts, very real for our philosopher, are related to their picture, just as the real objects are to their shadow pictures. In mathematics especially, the significance of the concept in relation to the picture of 'this' world becomes very clear: it is wholly directed to things that exist, things which without the help of mathematics could easily remain inaccessible to us.

According to this conception one could interpret the axioms as statements about 'original' mathematical truths, which are revealed to the mind's eye directly by a glance into the world of ideas. The theorems, on the other hand, are insights gained by deductions from the basic truths.

When occasionally, right up to modern times, mathematics is enthusiastically fêted by poets,[1] then the reason for this generally lies in the Platonic understanding of the nature of mathematics.

3. Noneuclidean geometry

All the enthusiasm about the mathematical 'world of ideas' cannot help over the difficulties which the fixing of a system of axioms for a mathematical theory presents. Which of the mathematical theorems are 'original' truths and which require a proof? In the *Elements of Euclid*[2] the following theorem appears as the fifth

---

[1] Two examples: Novalis says: Pure mathematics is religion. In *Les chants de Maldoror* by the Comte de Lautréamont (1846–70) we read: "La terre ne lui montre que des illusions et des fantasmagories morales; mais vous, ô mathématiques concises, par l'enchaînement rigoureux de vos propositions tenaces et la constance de vos lois de fer, vous faites luire, aux yeux éblouis, un reflet puissant de cette vérité suprême dont on remarque l'empreinte dans l'ordre de l'univers."

[2] The *Elements of Euclid* date from the fourth century B.C. This textbook collects together the mathematical knowledge of that time and was in use well into the nineteenth century as a geometry textbook in our schools.

postulate to the basic theorems of geometry, requiring no proof:[1]
"When a straight line meets two straight lines and forms with
them two interior angles on the same side whose sum is smaller
than two right angles, then the two lines meet if they are extended
on this side."

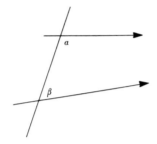

FIG. 1.

Many mathematicians were of the opinion that this theorem
should be deducible from the remaining axioms and postulates.
For over two thousand years attempts have been made in vain to
do this.[2] Finally in the eighteen-twenties the mathematician
Lobatschewski (1793–1856) and Johann Bolyai (1802–60)[3] suc-
ceeded in establishing a 'noneuclidean' geometry. This is a geometry
in which Euclid's fifth postulate does not hold.

This theorem is also known as the parallel postulate, since one
can easily deduce from it that through a point there exists only *one*
line parallel to a given line (in the plane determined by the point
and the line). In place of the parallel postulate we have in noneuclidean geometry the 'noneuclidean parallel postulate':

Through every point P of a plane E there exist at least two lines
parallel to every line g of E.

Of course one can object that this theorem contradicts intuition:
the alternate angles α and α_1 formed by the line k intersecting the
lines g and h in A and B are equal (see Fig. 2). If through B one draws

[1] Euclid distinguishes between *axioms* and *postulates*. Today it is usual to
call all fundamental theorems of a mathematical theory *axioms*.
[2] See, for example, Bonolas.
[3] The Russian Lobatschewski and the Hungarian Johann Bolyai obtained
their results independently of one another. The first publication (1826) was
due to Lobatschewski. Before either of them, Gauss had conceived the idea
of a noneuclidean geometry, as we know from his letters.

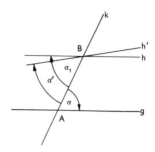

FIG. 2.

another line h' which forms with AB an angle α' different from α, then h' and g will meet somewhere.

Indeed one cannot deny that our experience suggests this view. Nevertheless one must admit that for angles α' which differ only little from α, the question cannot be decided by an 'experiment'. If $|\alpha - \alpha'|$ is sufficiently small, then the paper from all the paper factories on earth will not suffice to construct the point of intersection. Thus one cannot maintain that experience can answer the question as to the non-intersecting lines in the sense of Euclid. One still has to bear in mind the possibility of the existence of a non-contradictory theory with the noneuclidean parallel postulate.[1]

The objection has been raised against the Lobatschewski geometry that it is a purely formal construction. Even if the existence of exactly one parallel cannot be shown experimentally, there nevertheless remains the fact that for thousands of years classical geometry was used successfully for the description of physical laws. It is difficult to imagine that geometry with (at least) two parallels will be useful to the scientist.

But these objections of the conservative geometer are not tenable. One need only refer to the problems of astronomy. For astronomical dimensions it is not possible to realise straight lines by rulers or other mechanical devices. There remains only the possibility (which is also used for terrestrial measurements) of using the light ray as a straight line. But it by no means follows that a triangle formed by light rays with correspondingly large sides obeys the laws of

---

[1] We cannot establish this here. See, for example, Meschkowski (1) or Meschkowski (2). The second reference contains an exposition of the philosophical questions which result from the application of the different geometries to astrophysics. The freedom from contradiction of noneuclidean geometry can also be related to that of euclidean geometry.

euclidean geometry. Gauss, it is true, measured such a triangle on the earth and found that the sum of the angles (within the limits of errors of measurement) was indeed equal to two right angles. But by measurements on earth one can demonstrate only that for our 'small world' euclidean geometry is applicable. It is still an open question, which geometry is best suited to describe the regularities of the universe. We shall probably have to resort to a geometry which will differ from the euclidean not only by the parallel axiom. But whatever results research may establish one day, the consideration of the *possibility* of a different type of geometry will make it clear that the classical concept of the nature of mathematics is no longer tenable. In Plato's world of ideas there exists only *one* geometry, and Kant's conception of geometry and space also does not admit the possibility of a noneuclidean geometry.[1]

4. The formalism of Hilbert

The discovery of hyperbolic geometry and the resulting considerations about the problem of space have taught mathematicians[2] to regard their discipline as *the science of formal systems*.[3] Since it is not possible to make definite statements about the nature of mathematical objects, the modern mathematician renounces all *ontological* propositions. He no longer attempts (as Euclid did) to define the point and the straight line, and the world of ideas of Plato is no longer for him the essential prerequisite for his deductions.

He begins with certain 'objects' or 'elements' which are collected together into 'sets'. The 'properties' of the objects are determined by a system of axioms. From these axioms he derives by logical deduction further statements, the 'theorems' of his theory. The first significant work of this 'formalistic' school is Hilbert's book on the

---

[1] The geometry of Bolyai and Lobatschewski is also called 'hyperbolic geometry'. It differs in axiomatic construction from the euclidean only with respect to the parallel axiom. Naturally geometries with other divergences from the euclidean are conceivable. Consequently the plural term 'noneuclidean geometries' is meaningful.

[2] The discovery of antinomies in set theory has also contributed to this development. See, for example, Meschkowski (2). In modern physics also there is a corresponding turning away from all metaphysics which goes beyond the limits of the results of exact researches. Cf. March or Meschkowski (4).

[3] The overwhelming majority of modern mathematicians are 'formalistically' orientated. For other conceptions see, for example, Meschkowski (2), Chapter VII.

Foundations of Geometry, the first edition of which appeared in 1899.

Hilbert begins with the pithy statement:

"Let us imagine three different systems of objects: the objects of the first system we call points and denote them by A, B, C, ...; the objects of the second system we call lines and denote them by a, b, c, ...; the objects of the third system we call planes and denote them by α, β, γ, ...; ... We imagine the points, lines, planes in certain mutual relationships and describe these relationships by words like 'lie', 'between', 'parallel', 'congruent', 'continuous'; the precise and complete description of these relationships is by means of the *axioms of the geometry*."

These statements do not say anything about what the 'objects' of the three systems are. We are at liberty to imagine them to be anything we like, so long as they conform with the axioms (which Hilbert appends). In this way an 'implicit' definition of the objects of geometry is given. The freedom to imagine arbitrary things as points, lines, and planes is progressively limited by statements like the following:[1]

"Two distinct points A, B always determine a line a. Any two different points of a line determine this line."

In a letter to Frege,[2] Hilbert expressed his point of view thus:[3]

"If I imagine for my points any system of things, for example love, law, chimney sweeps ... and assume all my axioms as relationships between these things, then all my theorems, *e.g.*, that of Pythagoras, also hold for these things. In other words: every theory can always be applied to infinitely many systems of basic elements."

Of course Hilbert did not seriously contemplate doing geometry with the system 'love, law, chimney sweeps ...'. What he intended was to express as drastically as possible in this way his formalistic point of view.[4]

---

[1] These are the first two axioms of the Hilbert theory.

[2] Gottlob Frege (1846–1925) is known chiefly for his logical foundation of arithmetic.

[3] This and the following quotations from the exchange of letters between Hilbert and Frege are taken from the publications of Steck in the *Sitzungsberichte* of the Heidelberg Academy of Science, 1941.

[4] Elsewhere Hilbert has replaced 'points, lines, planes' by the system 'tables, chairs, beermugs'. This is mentioned by O. Blumenthal in his biography of Hilbert in the *Gesammelten Abhandlungen* of Hilbert (Berlin 1935, Vol. 3, pp. 388–429).

It will be clear that hereby the question as to the 'truth' of a mathematical theorem presents itself anew. When may we describe a mathematical theorem as true, if we reject all reference to metaphysics as well as to the 'real external world'? Also, what justifies us in placing certain theorems as 'axioms' at the beginning of a mathematical theory, if we can invoke for justification neither Plato's world of ideas nor physical insight?

For Hilbert, *freedom from contradiction* of a system of axioms is the decisive criterion for its usefulness. Besides this, *completeness* and *independence* of the basic theorems of a mathematical theory is demanded.[1] The *existence* of the mathematical objects, according to Hilbert, is secured by the freedom from contradiction of the axioms that describe the objects. It is well carefully to think over the following statement taken from the letters of Hilbert to Frege:

"If the arbitrarily postulated axioms do not contradict one another with all the consequences, then they are true; then the objects defined by the axioms exist. This, for me, is the criterion for truth and existence."

His correspondent, Gottlob Frege, does not share this view. He writes:

"I call axioms theorems, which are true, but need not be proved because their apprehension derives from a logically different source of knowledge, which one may call intuition. From the truth of the axioms follows automatically their freedom from contradiction. This does not require further proof."

According to this view proofs of the freedom from contradiction of a system of axioms are indeed superfluous. But this classical view of the nature of axioms presupposes a 'logically different source of knowledge'. In the case of geometry Frege refers to 'space intuition'. We shall leave aside the question as to which sources of knowledge are at our disposal for other mathematical disciplines. We know from a variety of examples that intuition can be illusory. We know further that a whole series of 'original truths' of classical natural sciences are inadmissible generalizations.[2] If such theorems, formerly generally accepted, as the 'law of causality' and the principle of the conservation of matter are today no longer considered as 'universally" valid, and if the belief in a general validity of euclidean

---

[1] See, for example, Meschkowski (2). There, also, an example is given of a proof of the freedom from contradiction of a formal system.

[2] See, for example, March, Stegmüller or Meschkowski (2) and (4).

geometry is shaken, then it is indeed doubtful from where we should take the 'true' theorems for the mathematical system of axioms.

It is therefore no nihilistic whim, if modern mathematicians renounce any metaphysical basis for their science. The limitation to sure dealings with 'formal systems' should rather be respected as an act of intellectual honesty. With such a preoccupation with what is absolutely sure mathematics becomes a discipline in which men of very different outlook can work together. One can ask, of course, whether behind the mathematical systems there is not more than is seen today by the researcher into the theory of knowledge. For the peculiar fact remains, that systems created by mathematicians and held by them, so to speak, in stock, again and again are found by the physicists to be useful for the description of the real external world. One may ponder about such relationships behind the mathematical formalism, but it is not to be expected that this will lead so readily as research in the realm of mathematics itself, to equally well founded and generally accepted results.

Thus let us adhere to the principle that the freedom from contradiction of a theory is the criterion for its validity.[1] Perhaps one can describe the point of view of Hilbert and the formalists still more precisely as follows: they have replaced 'truth' (in the metaphysical sense) by 'surety', namely the surety that by a correct application of the mathematical procedure with a suitable system of axioms, a contradiction can never occur.

Also with respect to 'existence' the modern view differs essentially from the classical one. To make this clear, we shall once more let Frege have his say:

"The sharpest contrast lies in our views about your criterion of existence and truth. But perhaps I do not fully understand your meaning. To clarify this point I suggest the following example. Let us suppose that the statements

1. A is an intelligent being;
2. A is omnipresent;
3. A is omnipotent

with all their consequences do not contradict one another. Could we then deduce from them that there exists an omnipotent, omnipresent, and intelligent being? To me this is not evident.

---

[1] This understanding is shared today by the majority of mathematicians. For the objections of the 'intuitionists' and the advocate of a 'materialistic' philosophy see, for example, Meschkowski (2) and (4).

The principle would be something like this: if the statements

'*A* has the property Φ',
'*A* has the property Ψ',
'*A* has the property X'

together with all their consequences are mutually non-contradictory (in general, whatever *A* may be), then there exists an object which possesses all the properties Φ, Ψ, X."

These sentences are contained in a letter which Frege wrote to Hilbert on August 25th, 1900. The publication by Steck does not tell us what Hilbert's answer was. Let us try, therefore, to meet Frege's objections from the standpoint of 'formalism'.

Frege is, of course, right in that one cannot, from the freedom from contradiction (assumed here) of certain statements about a 'being', conclude its existence. But mathematics (according to Hilbert) is not at all concerned with ontological statements and certainly not with proof about the existence or non-existence of higher beings. It makes perfect sense, however, to agree to regard 'objects' which have been implicitly defined by a system of axioms as 'existing', provided that the system does not involve contradictions. They 'exist' then as objects of a sensible theory. The more far-reaching question whether, for example, the points of a topological space correspond to real objects in the external world or in any 'world of ideas' is not the concern of mathematics.

5. Boolean algebra

From what has been said so far one might gain the impression that modern formalism represents an unavoidable but regrettable limitation of modern mathematical ideas compared with classical ones. But this is only one aspect of the matter. In fact mathematical formalism contains important possibilities for the extension of knowledge which were closed to classical mathematics.

In this connection one can refer to the fact that the examination of the independence and freedom from contradiction of systems of axioms has led to a significant insight into the theory of knowledge. Heinrich Scholz has referred to Gödel's important work on the freedom from contradiction of the theory of numbers as a 'critique of pure reason of 1931'. We cannot enter into these problems in detail.[1] Instead we shall talk about the possibility that formalism has opened up of arriving at an organic structure of mathematics by 'overlapping' theories. The introduction to the most important of these 'structures' is the task of this book.

To prepare for an understanding of the nature of the overlapping theories we shall, by way of introduction, report a few ideas of George Boole (1815–64). Bertrand Russell has said of this 'outsider' of mathematics that he 'discovered pure mathematics'.[2]

Boole had, in fact, already established the principles of mathematical formalism half a century before Hilbert. We have reported on the work of Hilbert first, since the necessity for a re-thinking of mathematical axiomatics can best be explained in connection with the basic questions of geometry. Indeed it was the discussion about the foundations of geometry which brought about the break-through to mathematical formalism. However in the attempt to formalize mathematical proofs according to the ideas of Hilbert, during the first decade of this century, one recalled the work of George Boole who, already in 1854 in his *Laws of Thought*, provided a formal treatment of logic.

After Peacock had pointed out in his *Treatise on Algebra* as early as 1830, that the letters x, y, and z in formulae such as

$$x(y+z) = xy+xz, \qquad x+y = y+x$$

need not necessarily stand for numbers, Boole in his *Laws of Thought* used letter symbols such as $x, y, \ldots$ as signs for 'the things that are the objects of our discussion'. In doing so the conditions for a formal treatment of logic were created, and Boole introduced for the propositional symbols an algebra which had a certain similarity with 'ordinary' algebra, but differed from it in a number of rules.

To give some idea of the wide range of possibilities of a mathematics formulated according to the notions of Peacock, Boole, and Hilbert we refer once more to the equations (1), (2), and (3) of p. 1.

We are accustomed to interpreting the distributive law (2) and the commutative law (3) as rules for calculation with (real or complex) numbers. But both laws are valid also for the *multiplication of segments*, as defined by Hilbert.

Let a and b be any two given segments and e an arbitrarily chosen 'unit segment'. We can then define 'multiplication' of the segments a and b as follows: in a rectangular coordinate system we make OA

---

[1] See Kleene or Meschkowski (2).
[2] For his biography see, for example, Meschkowski (3), Chapter VII.

on the negative x-axis equal to a, and OB on the negative y-axis equal to b. The unit segment $e = OE$ is marked on the positive y-axis. The line through B parallel to AE then meets the positive x-axis in a point C, where $x = OC$ is the 'product' of the segments a and b: $x = a \cdot b$ (see Fig. 3).

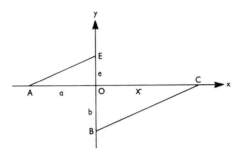

FIG. 3.

Note that by this procedure $x = a \cdot b$ is differently constructed from $x' = b \cdot a$. Nevertheless for this multiplication the commutative law

$$x = a \cdot b = b \cdot a = x' \qquad (3')$$

is also valid.

(3') is an equation between two *segments*, (3) an equation between *numbers*. The validity of (3') can be proved by elementary geometry. In the same way one can show that, for Hilbert's segment multiplication,

$$c(a+b) = ca+cb \qquad (2')$$

is also valid. Hilbert introduced this type of multiplication in order to justify a theory of area that does not make use of the continuity axiom. Here it is mentioned only as an example of the many ways in which equations (2) and (3) can be interpreted.

In vector algebra,[1] the inner product of two vectors a and b is defined by

$$a \cdot b = |a| \cdot |b| \cdot \cos \alpha \qquad (4)$$

where $|a|$ is the length of the vector a, $|b|$ that of b, and α is the angle

---

[1] See, for example, Peschl, *BI-Taschenbuch 15/15a*. There the notation *scalar product* is introduced for inner product.

between a and b (see Fig. 4a). The definition of the sum of two vectors is shown in Fig. 4b.

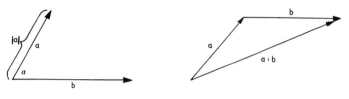

FIG. 4a, b.

In vector algebra

$$a \cdot b = b \cdot a \tag{3''}$$

and

$$c(a+b) = c \cdot a + c \cdot b \tag{2''}$$

also hold. This can easily be proved from the definitions of sum and inner product. In (2″) and (3″) a, b, and c are *vectors*. But the inner products, by definition (4), are again *numbers*. Hence the equations (2″) and (3″) are also equations between numbers.

However, whether we deal with numbers, segments, or with yet other objects, we can derive from equations (3) and (2) (see p. 1) the equation

$$(a+b)^2 = a^2 + 2ab + b^2 \tag{1}$$

Thus this relation is valid for the arithmetic of numbers, for Hilbert's segment multiplication and also for calculations with vectors (for the inner, or scalar, product).

Hence we need make only *one* calculation to obtain a result which is valid for *three* different branches of mathematics. We have here a simple example of the possibilities which are afforded by formalistic considerations. If one develops the theorems of overlapping theories (of structures) from their axioms, then every theorem obtained in this way can be applied *many times*, namely to all realizations of the structure.

CHAPTER TWO

Sets

1. Definition of sets

The mathematician is concerned with numbers and sequences of numbers, with points, segments, polygons, and vectors. He always deals with certain mathematical objects which, in one way or another, are considered as a whole. Such collections are called 'sets'. According to Georg Cantor (1845–1918), the creator of the theory of sets, a set is "a collection of certain well-defined objects, of our perception or our thought, into a whole". The objects thus collected together are called the *elements* of the set.

Modern mathematical set theory deals with sets whose elements are connected by certain relations which are fixed by axioms. In order to facilitate and to unify the presentation of this theory, certain basic facts of the theory will now be given.

The special achievement of Cantor lies in his extension of the theory to sets containing *infinitely many elements*. By introducing the concept of equivalence he was able to achieve ordering and the possibility of comparison in the realm of the infinite. It will not be possible to discuss in detail Cantor's theory of the 'power' of infinities.[1] We can confine ourselves to some basic facts of set algebra.

First a brief word must be said about Cantor's definition of a set. What strikes one is the generality of his concept of set, which is not confined to sets of mathematical objects. 'Objects of perception or thought' surely include umbrellas, radio sets, and also such abstract concepts as charm and ballot secrets.

In fact Cantor intended with his set theory to go beyond the bounds of mathematical theory. In a letter of February 1st, 1896 to his friend Father Thomas Esser in Rome, he emphasises that the

---

[1] See the works of Cantor or the *Einführung in die Mengenlehre und die Theorie der reellen Funktionen* of Alexandroff.

general theory of sets forms part of metaphysics. He writes:

> "The general theory of sets ... definitely belongs to metaphysics. ... This is not affected by the fact that, like all metaphysicists, I use illustrations from time to time for the clarification of metaphysical concepts. Also, the fact that the work that I am still writing is intended for publication in mathematical journals does not detract from its metaphysical character and content."

But it was precisely the generality of his concept of a set which was fraught with logical difficulties. If no restrictions are imposed in the definition of sets then one has to admit such sets as 'the set of all abstract objects' and also 'the set of all sets'. Such a set *contains itself as an element*; the set of all abstract objects is itself an abstract object and the set of all sets is also a set.

Bertrand Russell has shown that such terminology may lead to contradictions. In fact one has only to ask whether Russell's set, *i.e.*, 'the set of all sets that do not contain themselves as elements', does contain itself as an element. If one accepts that this is the case one at once comes to the conclusion that the set does not contain itself as an element, for the set comprises just those sets that are not contained as elements. On the other hand, if one assumes that the Russell set does *not* contain itself, then it must belong to the sets that are collected together in that set; hence the Russell set must contain itself as an element.

One can arrive at a useful theory of sets only if one interprets Cantor's definition as follows: *the elements or objects of a set must be 'determined' before they are collected together to form a set.* Expressed differently: the definition of objects of the set must not be given by means of the set. This excludes sets which are themselves contained as elements and there is no longer room for Russell's or similar antinomies.[1]

There are two distinct ways of defining sets.

1. We can enumerate all elements of the set.
2. We can define the set by stating a characteristic property of its elements.

The first possibility applies only to finite sets.

We now give some examples of the two cases. All sets will be denoted by capital letters and for finite sets the elements can simply

[1] For example that of Shen Yuting; see *Journal of Symbolic Logic*, Vol. 18, No. 2, June 53.

be shown between braces.

$$M_1 = \{1, 2, 3\}$$

$$M_2 = \{a, b, d, e, g, k\}$$

It is, of course, possible to define sets (using words of everyday language) by some characteristic property. For example:

M_3: the roots of the quadratic equation $x^2 - 7x + 12 = 0$;
M_4: the letters of the word CANTOR.

If x is an element of M, then we write

$$x \in M \tag{1}$$

If x does not belong to M, this is expressed by

$$x \notin M \tag{2}$$

Thus, for example, for the above sets M_1, M_2, M_3, M_4 we have

$$2 \in M_1, \qquad d \in M_2, \qquad 3 \in M_3, \qquad A \in M_4$$

and

$$4 \notin M_1, \qquad c \notin M_2, \qquad 1 \notin M_3, \qquad L \notin M_4$$

We now give a few examples of *infinite sets*:

Q: The set of all rational numbers. These are numbers which can be expressed in the form $x = p/q$, where p and q are integers and $q \neq 0$.

N: 1, 2, 3, 4, . . ., the set of all natural numbers.[1]

M_5: $x = 3n + 4$, $n = 1, 2, 3, \ldots$.

M_6:   The set of all rational numbers satisfying the inequality $1 \leqslant x \leqslant 2$.

M_7:   The set of all points in the complex plane interior to the unit circle. These points correspond to complex numbers for which $|z| < 1$.

M_8:   The set of all simple closed polygons in a plane E.

M_9:   The set of all points that lie inside the ellipse

$$9x^2 + 16y^2 = 144 \tag{3}$$

and in addition inside the circle

$$(x-4)^2 + y^2 = 4 \tag{4}$$

(see Fig. 5a).

---

[1] In the following we always use N and Q to denote the sets defined here.

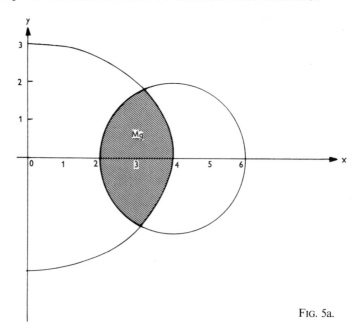

FIG. 5a.

M_{10}: The set of all points that lie inside the ellipse (3) *or* inside the circle (4) (see Fig. 5b).

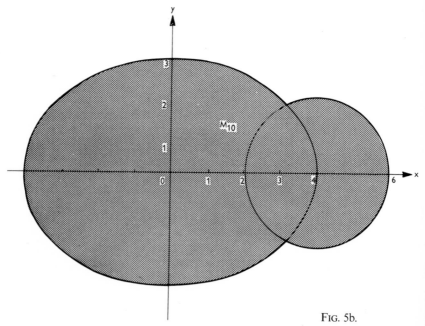

FIG. 5b.

2. Logical symbols

The description of given sets can be simplified by use of logical symbols. The propositions[1]

A : The point P lies inside the ellipse (3)
B : The point P lies inside the circle (4)

are combined in the definition of the set M_9 by the word *and*, and in the definition of the set M_{10} by the word *or*.

We introduce for the combination of two propositions by 'and' the symbol $\wedge$, and for 'or' the symbol $\vee$. The set M_9 is thus characterized by the proposition

$$A \wedge B \qquad\qquad (5)$$

More precisely, the set M_9 consists of exactly those points for which proposition (5) is true.

The conjunction 'or' is not always used in everyday language with the same meaning. Consider two examples.

(I) On April 3rd the Post Office charges for letters and telegrams will be increased. Whoever sends a letter *or* a telegram after April 3rd will have to pay more money.

(II) The teacher says to the pupil: be quiet *or* you will be punished!

In (II) the teacher confronts the pupil with an alternative. *Either* you are quiet, *or* you will be punished. *Exactly one* of the two events (according to the statement of the teacher) will occur. If the pupil is quiet then he need not fear punishment.

Example (I) is different. If somebody sends a letter and *in addition* a telegram, then he will, of course, have to dig more deeply into his pocket. In this case the 'or' corresponds to the Latin vel-vel, and in the second example to aut-aut.

We shall agree to use the symbol $\vee$ (which looks like v!) in the sense of the Latin vel. Thus the proposition

$$A \vee B \qquad\qquad (6)$$

is true if *at least one* of the two propositions is true. It is false if, and only if, both propositions A and B are false. Thus if the propositions A and B have the meanings ascribed to them above, then (6) is characterized by the region shown in Fig. 5b.

---

[1] Propositions will be denoted in the following by capital letters in heavy type.

If we denote the point with coordinates x and y by $P(x, y)$, then the definition of the sets M_9 and M_{10} can also be expressed as follows:

$$M_9 = \{P(x, y)/9x^2 + 16y^2 < 144 \wedge (x-4)^2 + y^2 < 4\}$$

$$M_{10} = \{P(x, y)/9x^2 + 16y^2 < 144 \vee (x-4)^2 + y^2 < 4\}$$

These definitions read: the sets M_9 and M_{10} comprise precisely those points that have the properties stated after the solidus sign. We give a few further examples of this type of definition.

$$M_{11} = \{x/x \in N \wedge 9 < x < 14\}$$

$$M_{12} = \{x/x \in Q \wedge 1 < x < 2\}$$

M_{11} is the set of the natural numbers between 9 and 14. This set can, of course, also be written in the form

$$M_{11} = \{10, 11, 12, 13\}$$

M_{12} is the set of rational numbers between 1 and 2

$$M_{13} = \{P(x, y)/x \in Q \wedge y \in Q \wedge x^2 + y^2 < 1\}$$

This is the set of all points with rational coordinates that lie inside the unit circle.

We now introduce two further logical connectives which will be useful in simplifying propositions about sets. The first is 'implication' denoted by $\Rightarrow$, which is usually read as 'if—then'. For the propositions

X: n is an even number,

Y: n can be expressed as the sum of two prime numbers,

the implication $X \Rightarrow Y$ means: *if a number n is even, then it can be expressed as the sum of two prime numbers.* This is the famous *Goldbach conjecture* which has not yet been proved.

If we replace X by the proposition

X^*: n is an odd number,

then $X^* \Rightarrow Y$ is an implication which is *false*. It is easy to convince oneself that, for example, the number 11 cannot be written as the sum of two prime numbers.

We still have to agree as to the 'truth value' that we must give to the implication

$$X \Rightarrow Y \tag{7}$$

when the proposition X is false. In this case the proposition (7) shall always be *true*. For example, let X, Y, and Y' be the following propositions

X: The moon is a pentagon
Y: $2 \times 2 = 4$
Y': $2 \times 2 = 5$

In accordance with our convention, the implications $X \Rightarrow Y$ and $X \Rightarrow Y'$ are both true. Expressed in everyday language we have

If the moon is a pentagon, *then* $2 \times 2 = 4$ (or $2 \times 2 = 5$). It may seem peculiar that this nonsensical sentence is considered to be *true*. But we must remember that the words of everyday language do not represent a legitimate interpretation of the logical symbols. This was already made clear when the symbol for 'or' was introduced. The implication (7) is a proposition which is false if, and only if, X is true and Y is false.[1]

Finally we introduce the connective

$$X \Leftrightarrow Y \qquad\qquad (8)$$

This says that X *and* Y *have the same truth value*. Thus either both are true or both are false. (8) reads: X if, and only if, Y.

Consider a few examples. The propositions

$$2 \times 2 = 4 \Leftrightarrow 3 + 3 = 6$$

and

$$2 \times 2 = 5 \Leftrightarrow 3 + 3 = 7$$

are both *true*. In the first case both the propositions that are connected by the symbol $\Leftrightarrow$ are true and in the second both are false. However, the logical relation

$$2 \times 2 = 4 \Leftrightarrow 3 + 3 = 7$$

is *false*, for on the left hand side of the symbol $\Leftrightarrow$ is a true proposition and on the right hand a false one.

Thus we adhere to the convention that the connectives expressed by the logical symbols

$$A \wedge B, \qquad A \vee B, \qquad A \Rightarrow B, \qquad A \Leftrightarrow B \qquad (9)$$

are not legitimately explained by corresponding words of everyday

---

[1] The advantage of this definition will become clear when the definition of a subset is given.

language. Their definition is given by the *truth value* that may be ascribed to the propositions (9) by the different possible combinations of the truth values of the propositions *A* and *B*.

We have defined the meaning of each individual symbol and it will be useful to collect these definitions in the form of a table, where the letters 't' and 'f' stand for true and false respectively.[1] From the following table one can then read the corresponding truth value of the connectives $A \wedge B$, $A \vee B$, etc.

A	*B*	$A \wedge B$	$A \vee B$	$A \Rightarrow B$	$A \Leftrightarrow B$
t	t	t	t	t	t
t	f	f	t	f	f
f	t	f	t	t	f
f	f	f	f	t	t

(10)

We see, for example, that $A \Rightarrow B$ is false if *A* is true and *B* is false. In all other cases $A \Rightarrow B$ is true. $A \wedge B$ is true if, and only if, *A* and *B* are both true, and so on. We denote the *negation* of a proposition by the symbol $\neg$ and read $\neg A$ as not *A*. Thus $\neg A$ is true if, and only if, *A* is false.

Finally we mention the symbols V and $\exists$, the all- and existence symbols, which are useful for the formulation of propositions. For example

$$V x(x + 1 = 1 + x) \quad \text{means} \quad \text{``For all } x, x + 1 = 1 + x\text{''},$$

and

$$(V x)(\exists y)(y > x) \quad \text{means} \quad \text{``For all } x \text{ there exists a } y \text{ that is greater than } x\text{''}.$$

3. Subsets

A set *A* is called a *subset* of *B* (written $A \subset B$) if every element of *A* is also contained in *B*. This definition can be expressed by means of

---

[1] We assume in propositional calculus that for every proposition *A* it is known whether it is true or false. Where this knowledge comes from is immaterial.

logical symbols as follows

$$\forall a(a \in A \Rightarrow a \in B) \Leftrightarrow A \subset B \tag{11}$$

It follows at once from this definition that every set *contains itself as a subset, i.e.*

$$\forall X(X \subset X) \tag{12}$$

If $A \subset B$ and there exists an element $b \in B$ which does *not* belong to A, then we say that A is a *proper subset of B*[1]. We give some examples. Let

$$A = \{1, 2, 3\}$$
$$B = \{1, 2, 3, 4\}$$
$$C = \{2, 3, 4\}$$

As usual let Q be the set of rational numbers and N the set of natural numbers. Then

$$A \subset B, \quad C \subset B, \quad A \subset N, \quad N \subset Q, \quad B \subset Q$$

In all cases the inclusion is *proper*. However the propositions

$$A \subset C, \quad Q \subset N$$

are clearly *false*.

The symbol $\subset$ must be carefully distinguished from the symbol $\in$ introduced on p. 17. To emphasize this, let us consider the set

$$D = \{1, 2, \{1, 2, 3\}\}$$

Its elements are the numbers 1 and 2 and the *set* $A = \{1, 2, 3\}$. In this case we have

$$\{1, 2, 3\} \in D, \quad \{\{1, 2, 3\}\} \subset D$$

where $\{\{1, 2, 3\}\}$ is a set whose only element is the set $\{1, 2, 3\}$. We also have

$$\{1, 2\} \subset D, \quad 2 \in D, \quad \{2\} \subset D$$

But the propositions

$$3 \in D, \quad \{2, 3\} \subset D$$

are *false*.

[1] Some authors (*e.g.* H. Lenz) write $\subseteq$ for the inclusion sign and reserve the symbol $\subset$ for *proper* inclusion. If, however, we adopt the formal definition (11), then we must choose the meaning given here for the symbol $\subset$.

It is convenient to define a set $\emptyset$, the *empty set*. This is the set that *contains no elements*. It is also called the *null set*.

One might object to this procedure, since sets were defined as *collections of objects*, and one cannot form a collection with nothing. This extension of the set concept is justified in the same way as the introduction of zero in the realm of numbers. Many propositions gain in simplicity by the introduction of the empty set.[1]

Moreover the introduction of the empty set makes it possible to define a set when it is not known in advance whether the set will have elements or not. For example, the *set of integer solutions* of the equation

$$x^3 - 8x^2 + 19x - 12 = 0$$

has the elements 1, 3, 4 and the corresponding set for the equation

$$8x^3 - 4x^2 + 2x - 1 = 0$$

is *empty*. This, however, need not necessarily be known when the set is defined.

Another interesting example is the set G of all even numbers that *cannot* be expressed as the sum of two prime numbers. According to Goldbach's conjecture this set is empty, but this has not yet been proved.

From the definition of a subset we obtain at once: *the empty set is a subset of every set*. Indeed, if the statement $a \in \emptyset$ is false for every a, then the implication in (11)

$$a \in \emptyset \Rightarrow a \in B$$

is true according to Table (10), whatever the set B may be. We thus have $\emptyset \subset B$.

The subset relation is transitive.

This means that from $A \subset B$ and $B \subset C$ it follows that $A \subset C$. This can be expressed more formally as

$$[A \subset B \wedge B \subset C] \Rightarrow A \subset C \qquad (13)$$

For if $A \subset B$, then by the definition (11),[2] we have for every $a \in A$

$$a \in B \qquad (14)$$

But since $B \subset C$ we have $b \in C$ for *every* element $b \in B$. Hence, by (14), we also have $a \in C$. Since a was an arbitrary element of A,

---

[1] See, *e.g.*, the theorem about the number of subsets on p. 25.
[2] The right hand side of (11) is true, so that the left hand side must also be true. Thus if $a \in A$ is true, by Table (10) $a \in B$ must also be true.

we have indeed $A \subset C$ (see Fig. 6).

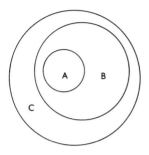

FIG. 6.

Note that, whereas the subset relationship is transitive, the relation of 'belonging' (as an element) is not. From $a \in A$ and $A \in B$ one cannot conclude that $a \in B$, as the following example shows.

$$a = 1, \quad A = \{1, 2, 3\}, \quad B = \{3, \{1, 2, 3\}\}$$

Of course it is possible in certain cases to have $a \in A$, $A \in B^*$, and $a \in B^*$, for example when $B^* = \{1, 3, \{1, 2, 3\}\}$.

The set $P(M)$ of *all* subsets of a given set M is called the *power set* of M. Its definition can also be written formally as

$$\forall X(X \in P(M) \Leftrightarrow X \subset M) \tag{15}$$

The power set of $A = \{1, 2, 3\}$ has eight elements $\emptyset$, $\{1\}$, $\{2\}$, $\{3\}$, $\{1, 2\}$, $\{1, 3\}$, $\{2, 3\}$, $\{1, 2, 3\}$, and the power set of $B = \{a, b\}$ contains the four sets $\emptyset$, $\{a\}$, $\{b\}$, $\{a, b\}$. Lastly the set with only *one* element ($M = \{a\}$) has a power set of two elements. These are the empty set $\emptyset$ and M itself. Generally we have:

The power set $P(M)$ of a finite set M of n elements contains 2^n elements.

We have already shown this to be the case for $n = 1, 2$, and 3. The proof for a general set is by the principle of *mathematical induction.*[1]

The theorem is true for $n = 1, 2, 3$. Let us assume that it is true for $n = k$. We must then show that it is also true for $n = k+1$. Let the $k+1$ elements of the set M_{k+1} be denoted by a_v ($v = 1, 2, 3, \ldots, k+1$). We divide the subsets of M_{k+1} into two classes. All the subsets that do *not* contain a_{k+1} belong to the class

---

[1] For this principle see p. 46.

K_1, which thus consists of the subsets of

$$M_k = \{a_1, a_2, a_3, \ldots, a_k\}$$

According to the induction hypothesis the number of these subsets is 2^k. If we now add to each of these sets of $P(M_k)$ the element a_{k+1} we obtain 2^k sets which all belong to $P(M_{k+1})$. These new sets and the sets of $P(M_k)$ together clearly form *all* the subsets of M_{k+1}. Thus the number of elements of $P(M_{k+1})$ is $2 \cdot 2^k = 2^{k+1}$, which proves our assertion.

4. Intersection and union

Definition. The intersection $A \cap B$ of two sets A and B is the set of all elements that belong to both sets, i.e.

$$x \in A \cap B \Leftrightarrow (x \in A \wedge x \in B) \tag{16}$$

The union $A \cup B$ is the set of elements that belong to at least one of the two sets A and B, i.e.

$$x \in A \cup B \Leftrightarrow (x \in A \vee x \in B) \tag{17}$$

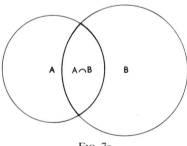

FIG. 7a.

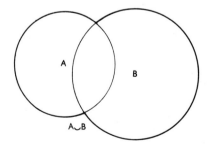

FIG. 7b.

We shall now give a few examples and for this purpose we define the sets

$$F = \{\tfrac{1}{2}, 1, \tfrac{3}{2}\}$$

$$G = \{x/x \in Q \wedge 0 \leqslant x \leqslant 2\}$$

$$H = \{x/x \in Q \wedge 0 < x < 2\}$$

$$J = \{1, 2, 3, \pi\}$$

$$K = \{x/x \in Q \wedge 1 < x \leqslant 3\}$$

where Q again denotes the set of rational numbers. Clearly[1]

$$F \cap G = F, \qquad F \cup G = G$$

$$F \cap J = \{1\}, \qquad F \cup J = \{\tfrac{1}{2}, 1, \tfrac{3}{2}, 2, 3, \pi\}$$

$$G \cap H = H, \qquad G \cup H = G$$

$$G \cap K = \{x/x \in Q \wedge 1 < x \leqslant 2\}$$

$$G \cup K = \{x/x \in Q \wedge 0 \leqslant x \leqslant 3\}$$

Sets of the type G, H and K are called *intervals*. The *open* interval $]a, b[$ is given by[2]

$$]a, b[= \{x/x \in Q \wedge a < x < b\}$$

The *closed* interval $[a, b]$ also contains its end points; thus

$$[a, b] = \{x/x \in Q \wedge a \leqslant x \leqslant b\}$$

With this notation we have

$$G = [0, 2], \qquad H =]0, 2[, \qquad G \cup K = [0, 3]$$

If only one of the end points belongs to the interval it is called *half-open*, and appropriate brackets are used, *e.g.*

$$K =]1, 3], \qquad G \cap K =]1, 2]$$

---

[1] Two sets A and B are *equal* ($A = B$) if every element of A also belongs to B and vice versa.

$$A = B \Leftrightarrow (x \in A \Leftrightarrow x \in B)$$

[2] Here we are regarding the intervals as sets of *rational* numbers. One can generalize the definition and regard the interval $]a, b[$ as the set of *real* numbers between a and b.

For the combination of sets by the symbols $\cap$ and $\cup$ the following rules hold

$$A \cap B = B \cap A \tag{18a}$$

$$(A \cap B) \cap C = A \cap (B \cap C) \tag{18b}$$

$$A \cap (A \cup B) = A \tag{18c}$$

To justify these relations we have to show that each element that belongs to the set on the left hand side of the equation is also an element of the set on the right hand side, and conversely. We shall confine ourselves to establishing equation (18c).

Let $a \in A$. Then we also have $a \in A \cup B$ and from the definition of the intersection it follows that $a \in A \cap (A \cup B)$. On the other hand, if we assume that a does *not* belong to A, i.e., $a \notin A$, then the proposition

$$a \in A \cap (A \cup B)$$

is false. Thus a belongs to the set $A \cap (A \cup B)$ *if, and only if*, a belongs to A. But this means that the two sets $A \cap (A \cup B)$ and A are *identical*.

Interchanging the symbols $\cap$ and $\cup$ in (18) one obtains the correct set of rules

$$A \cup B = B \cup A \tag{19a}$$

$$(A \cup B) \cup C = A \cup (B \cup C) \tag{19b}$$

$$A \cup (A \cap B) = A \tag{19c}$$

The proof of these is left to the reader.

The validity of the following formulae is immediately obvious

$$A \cup A = A \tag{20}$$

and

$$A \cap A = A \tag{21}$$

We shall illustrate the 'distributive law'

$$A \cap (B \cup C) = (A \cap B) \cup (A \cap C) \tag{22}$$

first of all by means of Fig. 8. The shaded portion of the figure represents the intersection of the set A with the union of B and C. This set can also be interpreted, however, as the union of the intersections $A \cap B$ and $A \cap C$.

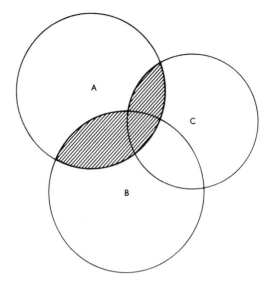

FIG. 8.

In order to prove (22) without reference to any pictorial representation we have to show that the sets on the two sides of the equation contain exactly the same elements. Assume first that an element x does not belong to A, *i.e.*, $x \notin A$. Then obviously x can belong neither to the set $A \cap (B \cup C)$ nor to the set $(A \cap B) \cup (A \cap C)$. The same is true if x does belong to A but not to B or C. In this case x is not contained in any of the three sets

$$B \cup C, \qquad A \cap B, \qquad A \cap C$$

Then x also cannot belong to $A \cap (B \cup C)$ or $(A \cap B) \cup (A \cap C)$. There remains the possibility that x belongs to A *and to at least one* of the two sets B and C. But in this case x belongs to *both* the sets that are connected by the equals sign in (22).

Interchanging the symbols $\cap$ and $\cup$ in (22) we obtain

$$A \cup (B \cap C) = (A \cup B) \cap (A \cup C) \tag{23}$$

This *second distributive law* is illustrated in Fig. 9. The shaded portion can be interpreted as the set on the left hand side or as the set on the right hand side of equation (23). The proof of (23) is similar to that of (22) and is left to the reader.

It is customary, to simplify the formal expressions, to omit the symbol $\cap$, just as in arithmetic, where the 'dot', which symbolises

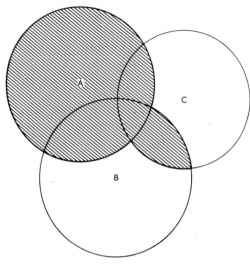

FIG. 9.

multiplication, is omitted. Equations (22) and (23) can then be written simply as

$$A(B \cup C) = AB \cup AC \tag{22'}$$

$$A \cup BC = (A \cup B)(A \cup C) \tag{23'}$$

(22′) brings out the formal analogy with the distributive law in the algebra of numbers

$$a(b+c) = ab+ac \tag{22''}$$

However, the formal analogue of (23′), viz.

$$a+bc = (a+b)(a+c) \tag{23''}$$

does *not* hold in ordinary algebra.

The formulae of 'set algebra' which have been derived so far can be used to derive other valid relations by purely manipulative methods. As an example consider the equation

$$(A \cup B)(A \cup C)(B \cup C) = AB \cup AC \cup BC \tag{24}$$

We first note that, according to (18b), it is permissible to omit the brackets in multiple products.

$$(A \cap B) \cap C = A \cap (B \cap C) = A \cap B \cap C = ABC$$

Thus it makes sense to write the 'product' of the three factors on the left hand side of (24) as we have done.

To prove (24) we apply repeatedly to the left hand side of the equation the distributive law (22′). Taking into account (18a), (19b), and (20) we then obtain

$$(A \cup B)(A \cup C)(B \cup C)$$

$$= [(A \cup B)A \cup (A \cup B)C](B \cup C)$$

$$= [AA \cup BA \cup AC \cup BC](B \cup C)$$

$$= AAB \cup BAB \cup ACB \cup BCB \cup AAC \cup BAC \cup ACC \cup BCC$$

$$= AB \cup BC \cup AC \cup ABC \tag{24a}$$

But by (19c)

$$AB \cup ABC = AB \cup [AB \cap C] = AB$$

Using (19a) we obtain equation (24) from (24a).

5. Functions

In the 1868 edition of the *Kompendium der höheren Analysis* by Oscar Schlömilch one finds the following definition of a function:[1]
    "If two variable numbers x and y are connected by an equation such that y occurs by itself on one side, *e.g.*

$$y = \frac{(x-a)^2}{2b}$$

then to any arbitrary value of x there corresponds a value of y which, since it is determined by the equation, is not arbitrary. In this case x is called the independent and y the dependent variable and, in order to indicate that it is x on which y depends, one calls y a function of x."

Even today most students enter the university with this notion of the meaning of a function which they acquired at school.[2] However, using the concept of sets, it is possible to give a much more general definition of a function.
    A set of pairs (a, b) is called a function (or a mapping) of the set A into the set B if the following conditions are satisfied:

[1] Brunswick, 1868, p. 2.
[2] There are, however, tendencies in modern school mathematics to introduce into the courses the formalistic aspect of mathematics. See the publications of the OEEC.

1) $a \in A$, $b \in B$;

2) *to each element $a \in A$ there corresponds exactly one pair (a, b).*

If *each* element of B belongs to at least one pair (a, b), then we speak of a function of A *onto* B.

Some authors use the following definition: *A function of A into B is a rule which assigns to each element $a \in A$ exactly one element $b \in B$.*

The first definition[1] involving pairs of elements has the advantage that it avoids the use of the concept 'rule' which is difficult to define precisely.

The functional relationship between the elements of A and B can also be expressed in the form

$$b = f(a), \qquad a \in A, \qquad b \in B \tag{25}$$

$b = f(a)$ is called the *value of the function corresponding to a.* Occasionally the statement 'f is a mapping (function) of A onto B' is written as

$$f : A \to B \tag{25'}$$

We now give a few examples.

(I). Let A be the set of all passport holders of a country and B the set of their passports. Then the mapping

passport holder $\to$ his passport

is a function of A onto the set B. This mapping is symmetrically unique (one-to-one).

(II). Let A be the set of the adults of a country and C the set of their representatives in parliament. Now the mapping

adult $\to$ member of parliament

is a function of A onto C which, however, is *not* one-to-one, since all adults of a certain constituency have the same member of parliament.

(III). Let X be the interval $[0, 2]$ and Y the interval $[0, 4]$. The set of pairs

$$(x, y) = (x, x^2) \qquad (x \in X, x^2 = y \in Y)$$

represents a function of X onto Y. This can also be written in the usual form

$$y = f(x) = x^2 \qquad (x \in X)$$

---

[1] See Lenz, p. 22.

It will thus be clear that a function defined in the sense of Schlömilch is also a function as defined here in terms of number pairs. There are, however, many functions which do not fit into Schlömilch's scheme. The following are examples.

(IV). Let X be the set of *real*[1] numbers between 0 and 1, and R the set of all real numbers;

$$X = \{x/x \in R \wedge 0 \leqslant x \leqslant 1\}$$

Then (x, y), where

$$y = \begin{cases} 0 \text{ for rational numbers } x \in X \\ 1 \text{ for irrational numbers } x \in X \end{cases}$$

is a function of X onto the set $Y = \{0, 1\}$.

(V). For finite sets X and Y the function can be defined by stating the mapping for each element. If

$$X = \{u, v, w, x, y, z\}, \qquad Y = \{3, 7, 9, 11\}$$

are given sets, then the mapping

$$\begin{array}{ll} u \to 3 & x \to 7 \\ v \to 9 & y \to 3 \\ w \to 11 & z \to 11 \end{array} \qquad (26)$$

defines a function of X onto Y. One can also say that (26) defines a function of X *into* the set N of the natural numbers.

(VI). Let P be the set of the simple closed polygons p of the plane E, R the set of the real numbers and R^* the set of the *non-negative* real numbers. Let $f(p)$ be the area of the (finite) region defined by p. $f(p)$ is then a function of the set P *into* the set R or *onto* the set R^*. Of the pairs $(p, f(p))$ the first element is in this case a *polygon* and the second a *real number*.

It is assumed here that the area is measured as is usual by real numbers. But according to Hilbert's theory one can also introduce 'segments' as a measure of area. In that case $f(p)$ represents a mapping of a set of polygons onto a set of 'segments'.

(VII). Let $F(a, b)$ be the set of functions $f(x)$ differentiable in an interval $[a, b]$ and $F'(a, b)$ the set of the corresponding derivatives. The set of pairs

$$(f(x), f'(x)), \qquad f(x) \in F(a, b), \qquad f'(x) \in F'(a, b)$$

[1] For the definition of real numbers see Chapter VIII.

is a function of $F(a, b)$ onto $F'(a, b)$. In the case of this function the sets involved are not sets of numbers but sets of *functions*. The mapping is not one-to-one, since the functions $f(x)$ and $f(x)+c$ have the same derivative $f'(x)$.

6. The cardinal number of a set

Of the mappings defined in II 5 only I, III and V were examples of one-to-one mappings.[1] Georg Cantor made use of the one-to-one mapping to introduce order among the different infinite sets and to make a comparison of these sets possible.

The set N of the natural numbers, the set Q of the rationals and the set R of the real numbers have the property of possessing an infinite number of elements. But N is a proper subset of Q, and Q is a proper subset of R. Is it possible to establish differences in type in the realm of infinity?

To achieve this we introduce with Cantor the notion of *cardinal number*. Two sets have the *same cardinal number* (or are *equivalent*) if a one-to-one mapping is possible between them. M is said to have a *higher cardinal number* than M' if there exists a one-to-one mapping of M onto a subset $M'' \subset M$, but there is no such mapping onto M itself.

We first give a few simple examples of equivalent sets. Among *finite* sets obviously all those are equivalent (of the same cardinal number) that have the same number of elements. But for infinite sets it is possible that a set M is equivalent to a proper subset $M' \subset M$. An example is the set N of the natural numbers and the set G of the even numbers. G is a proper subset of N, but nevertheless it is easy to establish a one-to-one correspondence between the two sets by the function $f(n) = 2n$. This correspondence can also be written in the form

$$
\begin{array}{ccccc}
1 & 2 & 3 & 4 & 5 \ \dots \\
\updownarrow & \updownarrow & \updownarrow & \updownarrow & \updownarrow \\
2 & 4 & 6 & 8 & 10 \dots
\end{array}
\tag{27}
$$

A set which is equivalent to the set N of natural numbers is called *countable*. The one-to-one correspondence of such a set with the natural numbers can also be expressed by attaching to the elements of the set the corresponding natural number n as a subscript, e.g., $\{a_n\}$, $n = 1, 2, 3, \dots$. A countable set expressed in this way is

---

[1] We note that Example III maps the interval $[0, 2]$ onto the interval $[0, 4]$. The inverse of *this* mapping is also unique. The fact that the function $f(x) = x^2$ is also defined for negative numbers need not be considered here.

also called a *sequence*. The sequence $G = G_n$ of the even numbers can by (27) be written simply as $G = G_n = \{2n\}$, $n = 1, 2, 3, \ldots$.

But the set[1] $Q[0, 1[$ of the rational numbers between 0 and 1 is also countable. To see this we write these numbers as fractions p/q $(p < q)$ and arrange them according to increasing denominators. Among the numbers with the same denominator the position in the counting scheme is given by the numerator. Thus we begin with zero; then follows the single number having the denominator 2 (viz. $\frac{1}{2}$); next the two numbers with denominator 3, and so on. Fractions which can be cancelled are omitted. In this way we obtain the following enumeration of the rational numbers between 0 and 1.

n	1	2	3	4	5	6	7	8	9	10	...
$r_n[0, 1[$	0	$\frac{1}{2}$	$\frac{1}{3}$	$\frac{2}{3}$	$\frac{1}{4}$	$\frac{3}{4}$	$\frac{1}{5}$	$\frac{2}{5}$	$\frac{3}{5}$	$\frac{4}{5}$	...

(28)

This 'counting' (28) represents a one-to-one correspondence of the rational numbers between 0 and 1 (including 0 and excluding 1) with the natural numbers. We shall denote this sequence by $\{r_n[0, 1[\}$. Thus

$$r_1[0, 1[= 0, \qquad r_2[0, 1[= \tfrac{1}{2}, \qquad r_3[0, 1[= \tfrac{1}{3}, \ldots$$

We can, of course, also 'count' the numbers between 1 and 2, between 2 and 3 and so on. We have only to put

$$r_n[1, 2[= r_n[0, 1[+ 1$$

The totality of all non-negative rational numbers can then be written as an infinite matrix[2] as follows:

$$
\begin{array}{ccccccc}
0 & \tfrac{1}{2} & \tfrac{1}{3} & \tfrac{2}{3} & \tfrac{1}{4} & \tfrac{3}{4} & \tfrac{1}{5} & \cdots \\
1 & \tfrac{3}{2} & \tfrac{4}{3} & \tfrac{5}{3} & \tfrac{5}{4} & \tfrac{7}{4} & \tfrac{6}{5} & \cdots \\
2 & \tfrac{5}{2} & \tfrac{7}{3} & \tfrac{8}{3} & \tfrac{9}{4} & \tfrac{11}{4} & \tfrac{11}{5} & \cdots \\
3 & \tfrac{7}{2} & \tfrac{10}{3} & \tfrac{11}{3} & \tfrac{13}{4} & \tfrac{15}{4} & \tfrac{16}{5} & \cdots \\
& & & & & & & \cdots
\end{array}
$$

The n-th row consists of the sequence $\{r_\nu[n-1, n[\}$, $\nu = 1, 2, 3, \ldots$. It is possible to rearrange the elements of such an infinite array in such a way that one obtains a single sequence $Q_1, Q_2, Q_3, \ldots$.

[1] Including 0, excluding 1.
[2] A *matrix* is a rectangular array of numbers.

In our case one simply has to take the numbers of (29) successively in the direction of the arrows as indicated, viz.

$$0, \tfrac{1}{2}, 1, \tfrac{1}{3}, \tfrac{3}{2}, 2, \tfrac{2}{3}, \tfrac{4}{3}, \tfrac{5}{2}, 3, \ldots \tag{30}$$

In this way one obtains a sequence $\{Q_n\}$, $n = 1, 2, 3, \ldots$. which consists of the set $\tilde{Q}$ of all *non-negative rational numbers*. By a slight variation of the procedure it is possible to enumerate the set Q of all rational numbers (positive and negative) but it is left to the reader to show this.

We have thus proved: *the set of all rational numbers is countable.* Alternatively *the set Q of rational numbers and the set N of natural numbers have the same cardinal number.*

This is a remarkable result. The beginner might object and maintain that there are 'far more' rational than natural numbers, so that perhaps Cantor's definition of cardinal number is not suitable to show up differences in the realm of infinity.

However this objection is not justified. It is true that Cantor's definition does assign the same cardinal number to infinite sets of quite different types, but it is nevertheless suitable for revealing 'steps' in magnitude in the infinite.

We shall confine ourselves to mentioning only *one* set which is of a higher cardinal number than all countable sets, and that is the set R [0, 1[of all real numbers between 0 and 1. Again we shall include 0 and exclude 1, although this is immaterial.

We first assume[1] that the set R [0, 1[is countable, so that it can be represented as a sequence $\{\rho_n\}$, $n = 1, 2, 3, \ldots$. Each element of the sequence would then be given by an infinite decimal fraction of the form $0 \cdot a_1 a_2 a_3 a_4 \ldots$. To make the representation unique we agree to use only *infinite* decimal fractions. Finite decimals, such as $0 \cdot 43$, can always be expressed in the form $0 \cdot 42999999 \ldots$, *i.e.*, as a decimal with infinitely many digits different from zero.

We then imagine the elements of the sequence arranged as shown

$$\rho_1 = 0 \cdot a_{11} a_{12} a_{13} \ldots$$
$$\rho_2 = 0 \cdot a_{21} a_{22} a_{23} \ldots$$
$$\cdots\cdots\cdots\cdots\cdots\cdots\cdots$$
$$\rho_n = 0 \cdot a_{n1} a_{n2} a_{n3} \ldots$$
$$\cdots\cdots\cdots\cdots\cdots\cdots\cdots \tag{31}$$

[1] We give here the proof using Cantor's 'diagonal process', which every mathematician ought to know. It should be mentioned, however, that Cantor gave another proof for the non-countability of the continuum: *Crelles J. f. Math.* **77**, 1874, pp. 258–62. See also Meschkowski (5) pp. 90–1.

where the numbers a_{ik} stand for one or other of the integers $0, 1, 2, \ldots, 9$. We assert that such an enumeration can *never include all* numbers of the set $R[0, 1[$. To show this it is sufficient to find one number $x \in R[0, 1[$ which is not contained in the enumeration (31). We put

$$x = 0 \cdot b_1 b_2 b_3 \ldots \tag{32}$$

and define the digits b_n of this decimal fraction as follows

$$b_n = \begin{cases} 1, & \text{if } a_{nn} \neq 1 \\ 2, & \text{if } a_{nn} = 1 \end{cases}$$

The decimal fraction defined by (32) does belong to $R[0, 1[$, but it is not identical with any of the numbers in the enumeration (31). If we assume, for example

$$x = 0 \cdot b_1 b_2 b_3 \ldots = 0 \cdot a_{n1} a_{n2} a_{n3} \ldots$$

then we can see at once that this equation cannot be true, since the two decimals must differ at least in the n-th place. Hence there exists no sequence $\{\rho_n\}$ which contains all numbers of the set $R[0, 1[$. The set $R[0, 1[$ is therefore *uncountable*.

We cannot pursue the interesting theory of cardinal number any further[1] and must confine ourselves here to a discussion of those theorems of set theory which are important for the basic structure of mathematics.

7. Ordered sets

If one had to arrange a group of people in some order, one could do this in a number of different ways. The group could be ordered according to height, so that A is placed before B if A is taller than B. Another possibility would be by a lexicographic ordering of their names. In this case Meier would be placed before Meyer, since i occurs before y in the alphabet.

One can also order the group according to age. We assume that no difficulty arises from two people having the same height, the same name or the same birth date. It is then possible, in one way or another, to introduce an order, such that for any two persons of a group we can always say whether A is before B or vice versa. For

---

[1] See, *e.g.*, the textbooks of Fraenkel or Alexandroff.

such an ordering we introduce the symbol $\prec$ ($a \prec b$ means: a 'before' b). This ordering satisfies the following axioms:

O_1: the propositions $a \prec b$ and $b \prec a$ are mutually exclusive.

O_2: order is transitive. From $a \prec b$ and $b \prec c$ follows $a \prec c$.

The ordering of a set M is said to be *antireflexive*[1] if for any two elements $x \in M$ and $y \in M$, $(x \neq y)$, a relation $x \prec y$ or $y \prec x$ is defined which satisfies the 'order axioms' O_1 and O_2. An apparently 'unordered' set of points is shown in Fig. 10a. We can introduce an

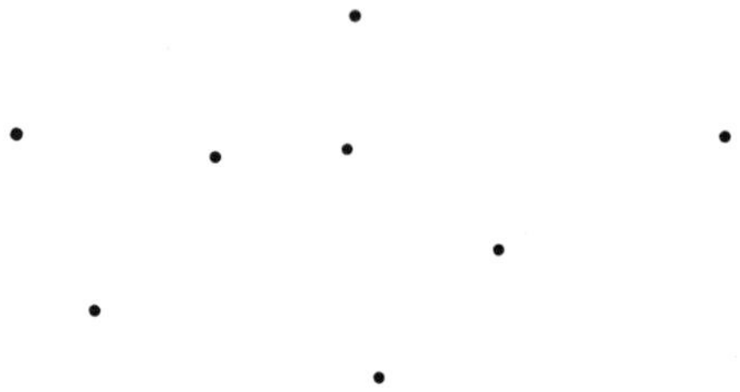

FIG. 10a.

ordering in a number of different ways. We can join all the points to an arbitrarily chosen point O (Fig. 10b) and measure the distances of all the points from O. If we are lucky these distances will all be different and in this case we can define an order such that $P_i \prec P_k$ if $OP_i < OP_k$.

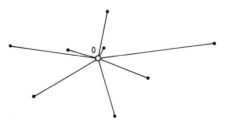

FIG. 10b.

Another possibility (Fig. 10c) is to drop perpendiculars from the points P_i on to an arbitrarily chosen straight line g. The length $d_i = P_i Q_i$ of the perpendiculars can then be used as a basis for the ordering; i.e., $P_i \prec P_k$ if $d_i < d_k$.

We give a few more examples of antireflexively ordered sets.

---

[1] The ordering is called antireflexive since, by O_1, $a \prec a$ is excluded. Other types of order relations will be dealt with in Chapter VI.

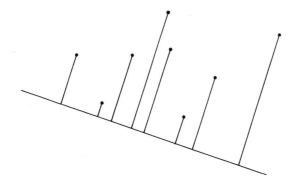

FIG. 10c.

(I). The set $Q[0, 1[$ of the rational numbers between 0 and 1 can be ordered by the relation $<$ or $>$.[1]

$$\{Q[0, 1[, \alpha\} : x \prec y, \qquad \text{if } x < y$$

$$\{Q[0, 1[, \beta\} : x \prec y, \qquad \text{if } x > y$$

The enumeration (28) can also be used as a basis for order.

$$\{Q[0, 1[, \gamma\} : x \prec y, \quad \text{if } x = r_n[0, 1[, y = r_m[0, 1[\quad \text{and} \quad n < m$$

(II). The set $S(A, B)$ of the points of a segment AB.[2]

$$\{S(A, B), \alpha\} : X \prec Y$$

if the intermediary relation AXY is satisfied.

(III). The set $\tilde{Q}$ of all non-negative rational numbers can be ordered as follows

$$\{\tilde{Q}, \alpha\} : x \prec y, \quad \text{if } x < y$$

For the definition of other orderings of the set $\tilde{Q}$ we can use the arrangement of the elements of $\tilde{Q}$ in the matrix (29). Let the general element of the matrix be a_{ik}, where i indicates the row and k the column in which it occurs. We then define

$$\{\tilde{Q}, \beta\} : x = a_{ik} \prec y = a_{lm}$$

---

[1] $\{M, \alpha\}$ and $\{M, \beta\}$ are different orderings of the set M.

[2] According to Hilbert's theory, for any three different points A, B, P of a straight line, *exactly one* of the intermediary relations ABP (B between A and P), BAP or APB is satisfied. A segment AB is the set of points P that lie between A and B.

if of the two differences

$$(i - l), \qquad (k - m)$$

the first which does not vanish is negative.
This means that the elements of the different rows of (29) are arranged one after another thus

$$\{\tilde{Q}, \beta\} : 0, \tfrac{1}{2}, \tfrac{1}{3}, \ldots ; 1, \tfrac{3}{2}, \tfrac{4}{3}, \ldots ; 2, \tfrac{5}{2}, \tfrac{7}{3}, \ldots \qquad (33)$$

Finally one can also use the diagonal counting process (30) as an ordering principle.

$$\{\tilde{Q}, \gamma\} : x \prec y, \quad \text{if } x = Q_m, y = Q_n \quad \text{and} \quad m < n,$$

where $\{Q_n\}$ is the sequence (30).

We call an antireflexively ordered set *well-ordered* if every non-empty subset of the set possesses a first element. Of all the orderings defined above only

$$\{Q[0, 1[, \gamma\}, \{\tilde{Q}, \beta\}, \{\tilde{Q}, \gamma\} \qquad (34)$$

are also *well-orderings*; the others are not.

Consider, for example, the ordering $\{Q[0, 1[, \alpha\}$ and the subset $]\tfrac{1}{2}, 1[$. This interval clearly has no smallest element and hence also no *first* element in the ordering α. The situation is different with the ordering $\{Q[0, 1[, \gamma\}$. Each subset Q' of $Q[0, 1[$ is a subset of the sequence $\{r_n[0, 1[\}$, and among all the numbers h for which r_h belongs to Q' there is, of course, a smallest. The element with this smallest number occurs in the ordering γ before all other elements of Q'. The ordering $\{\tilde{Q}, \gamma\}$ is similar.

But the arrangement (33) of the set $\tilde{Q}$ also has the character of a well-ordering. For each subset $\tilde{Q}' \subset \tilde{Q}$ there will be a first row i in the matrix (29) which contains elements from $\tilde{Q}'$ at all. Among these there will be an element a_{ik} with the smallest number k.

For well-ordered sets the following important theorem holds:

In every well-ordered set each element (with the possible exception of a last element) has an element which immediately succeeds it.

To prove this, we take an arbitrary element $m \in M$ and denote by M_m the set of elements that succeed m. Thus we have $x \in M_m$ if $x \in M$ and $m \prec x$. If m is not the last element, M_m is not empty, and as a subset of a well-ordered set it must possess a first element y.

Then $m \prec y$, and there exists no element $z \in M$ with the property $m \prec z \prec y$. y is thus the immediate successor[1] of m.

However we cannot assert that each element of a well-ordered set must have an immediate predecessor. A glance at the well-ordering (33) will make this clear. Among the numbers that 'precede' 1 there is no last one.

8. Problems

1. For all propositions A, B and C

$$\neg (A \wedge B) \Leftrightarrow (\neg A) \vee (\neg B) \tag{35}$$

$$A \wedge (B \vee C) \Leftrightarrow (A \wedge B) \vee (A \wedge C) \tag{36}$$

2. The set $A - B$ (A minus B) is defined by

$$[x \in A - B] \Leftrightarrow (x \in A) \wedge (x \notin B)$$

For this 'subtraction'

$$[(A - B) = A] \Leftrightarrow [(B - A) = B] \tag{37}$$

3. What follows for B from

$$A \cup B = A - B$$

and for A from

$$A - B = A \cap B?$$

4. Prove that

$$A \cup (B - C) \neq (A \cup B) - C \tag{38}$$

if $A \cap C \neq \varnothing$.

5. With the help of (35) and (36) prove that

$$A - (A - B) = A \cap B \tag{39}$$

---

[1] When, in the following, we speak of 'predecessor' or 'successor' in an ordered set M we shall, in general, omit the adjective 'immediate'. Thus "a is the predecessor of b" means

$$(a \prec b) \wedge (\forall x)\{(x \in M \wedge x \prec b \wedge x \neq a) \Rightarrow (x \prec a)\}$$

Correspondingly the statement "b is the successor of a" means

$$(a \prec b) \wedge (\forall y)\{(y \in M \wedge a \prec y \wedge y \neq b) \Rightarrow (b \prec y)\}$$

6. Prove that the set S of the points of a segment AB and the set G of the points of a straight line have the same cardinal number.

7. Prove that the set A of algebraic numbers[1] is countable.

---

[1] The algebraic numbers are defined as the solutions of algebraic equations

$$a_0 + a_1 x + a_2 x^2 + \cdots + a_n x^n = 0 \qquad (n = 1, 2, 3, \ldots) \qquad (40)$$

whose coefficients a_v are integers.

CHAPTER THREE

Rational Numbers

1. A system of axioms for integers

When votes are counted after an election a procedure often adopted is to register the votes cast for the individual candidates by some mark, for instance a vertical stroke. For each ballot paper with the names *A*, *B* etc. a stroke is entered in a list after the name as follows:

$$A: \quad ||||| \quad ||||| \quad ||||| \qquad B: \quad ||||| \quad ||||| \quad ||||| \quad ||$$

$$C: \quad ||||| \quad ||$$

The candidate with most strokes is elected.

Such 'sets of strokes' form particularly simple collections and they may be regarded as a class of equivalent sets. This means that the set of strokes after the name *B*, for example, is in one-to-one correspondence with the set of ballot papers that bear this name. But it is also equivalent to the set of people who voted for *B*.

Such lists of strokes can, of course, also be used for other purposes and in every case a one-to-one correspondence is set up between a set of objects and an equivalent set of strokes. The stroke sets

$$|, \; ||, \; |||, \; ||||, \; |||||, \; \cdots$$

are thus representatives of certain classes of equivalent sets. Often, however, when the sets contain very many elements, it is very inconvenient to prepare such sets of strokes. Even a foolscap sheet would be inadequate for this purpose. One then replaces the set of strokes by *numbers*, which may be regarded simply as symbols for the sets of strokes. 1 stands for $|$, 2 for $||$, 3 for $|||$, and so on.

In this way we have interpreted the natural numbers as symbols for certain 'representative' sets or also for a whole class of equivalent sets.

Computation with natural numbers can thus be reduced to the manipulation of classes of equivalent sets.[1] The procedure is, of course, cumbersome. It is simpler to confine ourselves to sets of strokes as representatives of classes and to examine the legitimacy of adding strokes to a given set of strokes. In this way one comes to an 'operative' justification of computation with numbers.[2]

Finally one can extract certain properties of the set N of natural numbers and collect them into a system of axioms. All further assertions about the set N are then deduced from these axioms. Since this axiomatic method is also used for other mathematical structures, it will be adopted here.

In order to facilitate the extension to negative numbers we shall formulate the axioms not only for the set N of natural numbers but more generally for the set Z of integers. The set N is then regarded simply as a subset of Z.

To formulate the axioms particularly succinctly we shall make use of the concepts of the theory of ordered sets. To the theorems and definitions of II 7 we add the following definition.

Let a be an element of an ordered set A. The set of all elements $a^* \in A$ for which $a \prec a^*$ is called the segment $A_a \subset A$ determined by a.

Thus, for example, for the ordering (II 33) of the set $\tilde{Q}$, the segment $\tilde{Q}_{\frac{1}{2}}$ is given by

$$\tfrac{1}{3}, \tfrac{1}{4}, \tfrac{3}{4}, \ldots; \qquad 1, \tfrac{3}{2}, \tfrac{4}{3}, \ldots; \qquad 2, \tfrac{5}{2}, \tfrac{7}{3}, \ldots$$

For the interval $J = [0, 1[$ the segment $J_{\frac{1}{2}}$ consists of the set of numbers of the interval that are greater than $\frac{1}{2}$. This segment has no least element in the ordering $\{Q[0, 1[, \alpha\}$.

Using the concept of 'segment' we can now define:[3]

The set Z of integers is a non-empty ordered set with the following properties:

A_1: *Z has no last element.*

A_2: *Every segment of Z is well-ordered.*

A_3: *Every element of Z has exactly one immediate predecessor.*

---

[1] See Lenz, Chapter II.

[2] See Lorenzen (1). The 'operative' justification of mathematics is (in its complete development) more troublesome than the axiomatic method, but it has the advantage that the axioms do not appear to be chosen arbitrarily.

[3] By this definition the existence of the set Z is postulated. It exists (we remember I 4) as an object of mathematical theory. Propositions of this kind are not ontological theses in the sense of the Platonic theory of ideas. The possibility that experiences in physics suggest such axioms is not under discussion here.

In this definition the set Z is assumed to be ordered. This means that a relation $\prec$ is given in Z, having the properties stated on p. 38. For the set Z (and all its subsets) we shall use the sign $<$ for $\prec$, and we shall read it as 'less than'.

We may picture this set Z as an infinitely long string of pearls with infinitely many pearls (Fig. 11).

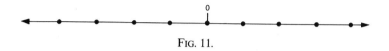

0

FIG. 11.

The order relation among the pearls of the string is given by the rule: $P \prec Q$ if P is threaded to the left of Q. There is, of course, no need for such a pictorial representation and we can deduce all the properties of Z from the axioms. But *if* such visual aids are used (and we shall do this from time to time) then we must be on our guard and justify all our conclusions by means of the axioms and not by the special properties of a 'model'.

Let x be an arbitrary element of Z and Z_x the segment determined by x. This segment has the following properties:

E_1: Z_x *has no last element.*
E_2: Z_x *is well-ordered.*
E_3: *Each element of Z_x with the exception of the first has exactly one immediate predecessor.*

E_1 is an immediate consequence of A_1. If Z_x were to have a last element y, then y would also be a last element of Z itself. The well-ordering of Z_x follows from A_2. Finally in the proposition E_3 we have to exclude the first element of Z_x since, according to A_3, its predecessor does belong to Z, but by the definition of Z_x it does not belong to Z_x.

We have shown in II 7 that in every well-ordered set each element (with the possible exception of a last element) has a successor. Now since any element $x \in Z$ belongs to all segments Z_y with $y < x$, x also has a successor. It is the first element of the well-ordered set Z_x.

Let us now select an arbitrary element $x \in Z$ and denote it by 0 (zero).[1] The elements of Z_x (each of which has a successor) can

---

[1] We can think of this as a specially marked pearl on our string, cf. Fig. 11.

be put into one-to-one correspondence with the set of strokes:

$$
\begin{array}{ccccc}
0' & 0'' & 0''' & 0'''' & 0''''' \ldots \\
\updownarrow & \updownarrow & \updownarrow & \updownarrow & \updownarrow \\
| & || & ||| & |||| & ||||| \cdots
\end{array} \tag{1}
$$

In this way we establish the existence of a non-empty set $N = Z_x = Z_0$, which has the following properties:

S_1: *N has no last element.*
S_2: *Every non-empty subset of N has a first element.*
S_3: *Each element of N with the exception of the first has exactly one predecessor.*

This set N is called the *set of natural numbers*. Its elements are denoted by the sets of strokes (1) or by the corresponding symbols $1, 2, 3, \ldots$.

The above theorems S_1, S_2, and S_3 are the axioms of Erhard Schmidt for the set of natural numbers.[1] He used this system in his lectures (in the nineteen twenties in Berlin) without publishing it. Only in 1950 was this system of axioms reported by one of his pupils, Hans Rohrbach.[2] A similar system was used independently by S. Kaczmarz[3] as a basis for arithmetic.

Every number $z \in Z$ has (as an element of a well-ordered segment) a successor z' and, by A_3, a predecessor $'z$. Successor and predecessor are obviously connected by

$$
('z)' = '(z') = z \tag{2}
$$

This relation is valid for all elements $n \in N$ with the exception of $n = 1$. This number has no predecessor in N.[4]

In the following we shall first deal exclusively with the set N of natural numbers and only later (in III 4) shall we return to the more extensive set Z.

2. The principle of mathematical induction

In II 3 we proved by 'mathematical induction' a theorem which holds for all natural numbers n. We shall now justify this method

---

[1] In our exposition they appear as theorems that follow from the axioms A_1, A_2, and A_3.
[2] *Math. Nachr.* **4** (1950), pp. 315–21. See also Feigl-Rohrbach.
[3] *J. London Math. Soc.* **7** (1932), pp. 179–82.
[4] It is customary to write $n+1$ for n'. However we first want to base addition on our axioms. Besides, the notion of 'successor' in a number sequence can be introduced before the definition of addition.

of proof by means of our axioms. It is based on the following *theorem of mathematical induction.*

(J_1) *Let M be a subset of N with the following properties:*
   1) *the number* 1 *belongs to M;*
   2) *if $n \in M$, then $n' \in M$ also.*
   Then $M = N$.

For the proof we consider the complementary set M^* of M with respect to N. This is the set of elements of N which do *not* belong to M. Thus

$$x \in M^* \Leftrightarrow [x \notin M \wedge x \in N]$$

Let us assume that M^* is not empty. Since N is well-ordered, M^* will then have a first element m.

We have further $1 < m$, since according to condition 1), $1 \in M$. Hence it follows from S_3 that m has a predecessor n. Thus $n \in M$, $n' = m$.

But by condition 2) from $n \in M$ it follows that $n' = m \in M$, which contradicts the hypothesis that m belongs to the complementary set M^*. Hence the assumption that M^* is not empty is false. But this means that M and N are identical.

The theorem just proved is often formulated as follows.

(J_2) *Let a proposition $A(n)$ be true for the number $n = 1$. If from the truth of the proposition for the natural number k the truth for the successor k' always follows, then the proposition is true for all natural numbers.*

In fact, let M be the subset of numbers for which the proposition $A(n)$ is true. Then by the conditions of (J_2) and the theorem which we have just proved $M = N$ and consequently $A(n)$ is true for all natural numbers.

In the literature on the foundations of arithmetic one often finds, instead of Schmidt's system which we have discussed here, a system of axioms for the set N of natural numbers which is due to Peano[1], viz.

P_1: 1 *is a natural number.*
P_2: *to each number $n \in N$ there exists a successor n', which also belongs to N.*
P_3: $n' \neq 1$.

---

[1] The system is usually called after Peano. But it was given earlier (in a similar form) by Dedekind in his work *Was sind und was sollen die Zahlen?*

P_4: *from $n' = m'$ it follows that $n = m$.*

P_5: *a set M of natural numbers which contains the number 1, and contains m' whenever it contains m, is identical with N.*

It is easy to show that Peano's axioms can be derived from Schmidt's and vice versa. We shall content ourselves with giving the derivation of Peano's system from that of Schmidt.

Axiom P_5 is the theorem of mathematical induction which we have just proved. The validity of P_1 is a consequence of the well-ordering. The existence of a successor (P_2) also follows from a general theorem on well-ordered sets (see p. 40).

If $n' = 1$ for any natural number, then 1 would have a predecessor. But 1 is the first number of the well-ordered set N. Hence P_3 holds.

To prove P_4, we assume that the successors of two different numbers m and n are equal, *i.e.*, $m' = n'$. We then have, by (2)

$$m = '(m') = '(n') = n$$

contrary to hypothesis, so that P_4 is also proved.

We leave it to the reader to show that Schmidt's axioms can be derived from those of Peano.[1]

3. Addition and multiplication of natural numbers

The principle of mathematical induction can also be used for *definitions*. We define the sum $s(a, b)$ of two natural numbers a and b as follows:

Let a be an arbitrary natural number. The sum $s(a, b)$ for all natural numbers b is given by

$$s(a, 1) = a'$$
$$s(a, b') = (s(a, b))' \qquad (3)$$

Writing $a + b$ for $s(a, b)$, (3) takes the form

$$a + 1 = a'$$
$$a + b' = (a + b)' \qquad (3')$$

---

[1] Cf. the work of H. Rohrbach already mentioned. There it is also shown that one can reduce the axiomatic assumptions for the system of Schmidt. One need not assume the transitivity of the relation $<$, but only that if $a < b$, then $b < a$ is false.

The notation used in (3), which will strike the beginner as unusual, lends precision to the mental picture that when adding a natural number b one simply has to add the unit (the stroke in our sets of strokes) b times. $a+1$ is the successor of a which is obtained by adding a further stroke. If $a+b$ has already been reached by the addition of strokes, then one obtains $a+b'$ by forming the successor of the number $(a+b)$ already reached.

In this way $a+b$ is defined for all natural numbers. For, let B be the set of numbers b for which the sum $a+b$ is defined by (3) or (3'). Then $1 \in B$ and for $b \in B$ it follows from the second equation (3') that $b' \in B$. By theorem (J_1) (p. 47) it follows that B is identical with the set N of natural numbers.

We may add that the function[1] $s(a, b)$ is *uniquely determined* by the condition (3). If there were a second function $t(a, b)$ with the properties

$$t(a, 1) = a'$$
$$t(a, b') = (t(a, b))' \tag{3''}$$

then by (3') and (3'') we should have $s(a, 1) = t(a, 1)$. Now let G be the set of natural numbers for which $s(a, b) = t(a, b)$. Then $1 \in G$. If $k \in G$, then $s(a, k) = t(a, k)$ and by (3') and (3'') it follows that $s(a, k') = t(a, k')$. By the principle of mathematical induction it follows that G is identical with N. Thus $s(a, b)$ and $t(a, b)$ are equal for all natural numbers.

For calculations with sums as defined by (3') the following rules apply

$$(a = b) \Rightarrow (a+c = b+c) \tag{4}$$
$$(a+b)+c = a+(b+c) \tag{5}$$
$$a+b = b+a \tag{6}$$

They can be proved by induction and we shall limit ourselves to establishing (6).[2] First we justify the special case

$$a+1 = 1+a \tag{6'}$$

This equation is true for $a = 1$. We assume that it is also true for $a = k$

$$k+1 = 1+k \qquad \text{,}$$

---

[1] For a fixed a, $s(a, b)$ is a function of b. It maps N on N.
[2] For this we assume the validity of (5), which is proved by induction on c.

Then by (3′)

$$1 + k' = (k+1)'$$

or

$$1 + (k+1) = (k+1) + 1$$

Hence by (J_2), (6′) is true for all natural numbers a. This is the basis for a second application of the induction principle. By (6′), (6) is true for $b = 1$. Let us assume that (6) is true for $b = k$

$$a + k = k + a \qquad (7)$$

Then by (3′) and (7)

$$a + k' = (a+k)' = (k+a)'$$

or

$$a + (k+1) = (a+k) + 1 = (k+a) + 1$$

From this, by (5) and (6′), it follows that

$$a + (k+1) = k + (a+1) = k + (1+a) = (k+1) + a$$

Hence (6) is proved by a twofold application of the principle of induction.

Multiplication of natural numbers can also be defined recursively, i.e., by induction.

Let a be an arbitrary natural number. For every natural number b, the product p(a, b) is a number which satisfies the induction hypothesis

$$p(a, 1) = a, \qquad p(a, b') = p(a, b) + a \qquad (8)$$

The numbers a and b are called the *factors* of the product $p(a, b) = a \cdot b$ (a times b). The dot between a and b can be omitted, so that $a \cdot b = ab$.

Using this notation we have instead of (8)

$$a \cdot 1 = a, \qquad a(b+1) = ab + a \qquad (8')$$

Just as for addition one can also show here that the result of the operation $p(a, b)$ is *uniquely* determined by the induction hypothesis (8).

For the multiplication thus defined the following rules hold

$$a \cdot b = b \cdot a \qquad (9)$$

$$(a = b) \Rightarrow (ac = bc) \qquad (10)$$

$$a(b+c) = ab + ac \qquad (11)$$

$$a(bc) = (ab)c \qquad (12)$$

By the last rule, one can omit the brackets in a product altogether

$$a(bc) = abc, \qquad (ab)(cd) = (abc)d = a(bcd) = abcd$$

Here too all the proofs are by the method of induction. We can, therefore, be brief and leave some of the deductions to the reader.

The *commutative law* (9) (analogously to the commutative law for addition (6)) is proved in two steps. One first proves the formula

$$a \cdot 1 = 1 \cdot a = a$$

and from this the general law (9).

We shall give the proof of the *distributive law* (11) only. The proof is by induction on c.

Clearly (11) is true for $c = 1$, since by (8′)

$$a(b+1) = ab + a = ab + a \cdot 1 \qquad (13)$$

Let us assume that (11) is true for $c = k$

$$a(b+k) = ab + ak \qquad (14)$$

From this we must prove that the formula holds for $k+1$. Now by (3′), (8′), (13), and (14) we have

$$a(b+k') = a(b+k)' = a(b+k) + a = ab + ak + a$$
$$= ab + a(k+1) = ab + ak'$$

Thus (11) is true for all natural numbers c.

We shall next derive a number of order relations ('inequalities') which hold for addition and multiplication of natural numbers. To do this we refer to theorems O_1 and O_2 for ordered sets (II 7). For the order relation $<$ in the set N they can be written in the form

$$(a < b) \Leftrightarrow \neg(b < a) \qquad (15a)$$
$$[(a < b) \wedge (b < c)] \Rightarrow (a < c) \qquad (15b)$$

It will be useful to introduce the symbol $\leqslant$. $a \leqslant b$ means that $a < b$ or $a = b$.

$$(a \leqslant b) \Leftrightarrow (a < b) \vee (a = b)$$

Clearly for natural numbers a and b

$$(a < b) \Rightarrow (a' \leqslant b) \qquad (16)$$

For addition and multiplication of natural numbers we have further[1]

$$(a < b) \Rightarrow [(a+c) < (b+c)] \tag{17}$$

$$a < a+b \tag{18}$$

$$(a+c < b+c) \Rightarrow (a < b) \tag{19}$$

$$a < a \cdot b \text{ for } b > 1 \tag{20}$$

$$(a < b) \Rightarrow (ac < bc) \tag{21}$$

$$(ac < bc) \Rightarrow (a < b) \tag{22}$$

$$(a+c = b+c) \Rightarrow (a = b) \tag{23}$$

The proofs of these statements are again based on the principle of mathematical induction. We shall confine ourselves to proving (18) and (21).

Since $a < a' = a+1$, (18) is true for $b = 1$. If (18) is true for $b = k$, i.e., $a < a+k$, then by the monotonic property of the $<$-relation $a < (a+k)' = a+(k+1)$, so that (18) is proved.

We prove (21) by induction on c. Since $a \cdot 1 = a$ the formula is true for $c = 1$. Let it be true for $c = k$. For $a < b$ we then have

$$ak < bk$$

By (17) it follows that

$$ak' = a(k+1) = ak+a < bk+a < bk+b = bk'$$

Hence for $a < b$ the inequality $ac < bc$ holds for all natural numbers c.

4. Addition of integers

We now turn to the question, under what conditions has the operation of addition in the set N an *inverse*? Stated more explicitly:

Given two arbitrary natural numbers a and b, under what conditions does there exist a natural number c such that[2]

$$a+c = b \tag{24}$$

---

[1] Instead of $a < b$ we also write $b > a$ (b 'greater than' a). $b \geqslant a$ means that $b > a$ or $b = a$.

[2] Negative numbers are usually defined by means of number pairs. See, *e.g.*, Feigl-Rohrbach, Pickert-Görke in the *Handbuch* of Behnke-Fladt-Süss, Vogel. The introduction of the system of axioms in III 1 makes the obvious method of recursion possible.

Clearly (24) has no solution if $b \leqslant a$, for in this case $a+c > a \geqslant b$ by (18). Let us assume, then, that $a < b$. We can then establish by induction the existence of a number c having the property (24). For $b = a'$, $c = 1$ is a solution of (24). Let us assume that $a+c = k$, where $k \geqslant a'$, has a solution. Then

$$a+c' = (a+c)' = k'$$

We then have a solution c' for the case $b = k'$. Thus there exists a solution of the equation (24) (for the 'unknown' c) when $a < b$.

There cannot be more than one solution. For if

$$a+d = a+c = b$$

it follows by (23) that $c = d$.

The solution of the equation (24) (for the case $a < b$) is called the *difference b minus a* and is written

$$c = b-a \tag{25}$$

The formation of such a difference is called *subtraction*, which can be interpreted as the inverse of addition. For by (24) and (6) we have

$$(b-a)+a = a+(b-a) = b \tag{26}$$

In order to define the difference of two numbers *without restriction* it is necessary to extend the range of the (natural) numbers. To do this we have only to go back to the set Z of integers defined in III 1. In this set, which was specified by the axioms A_1, A_2 and A_3, we chose an arbitrary element as the number zero (0) and the following elements in the given ordering as the natural numbers $1, 2, 3, \ldots$. We shall now give names to the elements *preceding* zero. For the predecessor $'0$ of the number 0 we write -1, for $''0$ we write -2, and so on. Hence the 'pearls' of the string of Fig. 11 have been assigned names as shown in Fig. 12. The numbers $x < 0$ are called *negative numbers*.[1]

For negative numbers the following ordering obviously holds

$$(-m) < (-n) \quad \text{if} \quad n < m \tag{27}$$

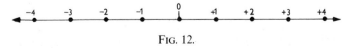

FIG. 12.

[1] Correspondingly the *natural* numbers are also called *positive* numbers.

We shall now define *addition* for arbitrary integers and we first extend the definition of III 3 to the number 0. We define

$$x+0 = x \qquad (28)$$

for all integers x.[1]

We can then generalize the definition of addition (see (3')) as follows

$$x+0 = x$$
$$x+b' = (x+b)' \qquad (29)$$

In particular we then have, for all natural numbers a,

$$a+1 = a+0' = (a+0)' = a'$$

as in the old definition (3'). This means that for the natural numbers $x = a$, (29) leads to the same computation rules as (3'). However, (29) can be extended to arbitrary integers x, where b, as before, denotes a natural number.

In order to be able to replace b by a negative number we supplement (29) by a second definition

$$x+0 = x$$
$$x+'y = '(x+y) \qquad (30)$$

One can see at once by induction that (30) holds for natural numbers $y = b$. But (30) is also valid for negative numbers $y = -b$ and gives a recursive definition for the addition of negative numbers. We have

$$x+(-1) = x+'0 = '(x+0) = 'x$$
$$x+(-2) = x+'(-1) = '(x+(-1)) = ''x$$
$$x+(-3) = x+'(-2) = '(x+(-2)) = '''x$$

$$\dots\dots\dots\dots\dots\dots\dots\dots\dots\dots\dots\dots\dots\dots$$

In particular we have $3+(-3) = '''3 = 0$. By mathematical induction it is easy to show that, for all natural numbers a

$$a+(-a) = 0 \qquad (31)$$

It must be examined to what extent the rules (4), (5), and (6) remain valid for the addition of negative numbers. They do indeed

[1] In the following we shall denote *integers* by $z, y, x, w, \dots$ and *natural* numbers by $a, b, c, \dots.$

hold. To see this one has only to consider the formal analogy between the definitions (29) and (30). To obtain the proofs for the generalizations of (4), (5), and (6) one simply has to replace the primes after the numbers (for the successor) by primes in front of the numbers (for the predecessor) in the proofs of (4), (5), and (6).

We shall confine ourselves to justifying the associative law

$$(x+y)+(-c) = x+(y+(-c)) \tag{5'}$$

for negative numbers $-c$.

For $c = 1$ we have, by (30)

$$(x+y)+(-1) = {}'((x+y)+0) = {}'(x+y) = x+{}'y = x+(y+(-1))$$

Thus (5') is true for $c = 1$. Assume that (5') is true for $c = k$; then

$$(x+y)+(-k) = x+(y+(-k)) \tag{5''}$$

Hence by (30) and (5'')

$$(x+y)+{}'(-k) = {}'((x+y)+(-k)) = {}'(x+(y+(-k)))$$
$$= x+{}'(y+(-k)) = x+(y+{}'(-k))$$

or[1)]

$$(x+y)+(-(k+1)) = x+(y+(-(k+1)))$$

Hence by induction (5') is proved for all natural numbers c. Since one can prove similarly, using (29), that

$$(x+y)+c = x+(y+c)$$

we have

$$(x+y)+z = x+(y+z) \tag{32}$$

for arbitrary integers x, y and z.

Similarly we can prove that

$$(x = y) \Rightarrow (x+z = y+z) \tag{33}$$

and

$$x+y = y+x \tag{34}$$

Using (34), (32), and (2) it is easy to prove that, for all integers u and v

$${}'u+v' = u+v \tag{35}$$

[1)] From (27) it is easy to see that the predecessor of $(-k)$ is $-(k+1)$.

For

$$'u + 'v = 'u + (v+1) = 'u + (1+v) = ('u+1) + v$$
$$= ('u)' + v = u + v$$

We can now show that the problem inverse to addition can be solved for all integers without restriction. For arbitrary positive numbers a and b

$$(a + (-b)) + b = a \tag{36}$$

The induction process for (36) is as follows: first

$$(a + (-1)) + 1 = ('a)' = a$$

Let (36) be true for $b = k$, viz.

$$(a + (-k)) + k = a \tag{37}$$

Then by (35) and (37)

$$a + (-(k+1)) + (k+1) = (a + '(-k)) + k' = '(a + (-k)) + k'$$
$$= (a + (-k)) + k = a$$

Hence (36) holds for all natural numbers b.

If we denote the solution of the equation

$$x + b = a$$

by $x = a - b$, then by (36) we have

$$a - b = a + (-b) \tag{38}$$

This time, however, we have placed no restrictions on the numbers a and b. Thus subtraction $b - a$ is possible for all integers, even if $b \leqslant a$. In this case, of course, the solution $b - a = b + (-a)$ will be negative or zero.

If we replace a by an arbitrary integer z, we obtain

$$x = z - b = z + (-b)$$

as the solution of the equation $x + b = z$.

We shall now replace b by an integer y. To do this we define

$$-(-b) = b \tag{39}$$

for all natural numbers b. We then have as solution of the equation $x + y = z$ in the case $y = -b$

$$x = z - y = z + (-y) = z + (-(-b)) = z + b$$

For
$$(z+b)+y = (z+b)+(-b) = (z+b)-b = z$$

Here too (just as for natural numbers) the difference is *uniquely* determined. The proof is left to the reader.

For later use we mention the equation

$$(-a)+(-b) = -(a+b) \tag{40}$$

which can be proved, for example, by (31). We have

$$(a+b)+(-(a+b)) = 0 \tag{41}$$

and by (32) and (34) we also have

$$(a+b)+((-a)+(-b)) = 0 \tag{42}$$

Hence by (41) and (42)

$$0-(a+b) = -(a+b) = (-a)+(-b)$$

5. Multiplication of integers

The recursive definition (8′) of multiplication can easily be generalized to the case in which the first factor a is an arbitrary *integer.*

$$x \cdot 1 = x$$
$$x(b+1) = xb' = xb+x \tag{43}$$

For negative integers $x = -a$ we obtain from this the law

$$(-a) \cdot b = -(ab) \tag{44}$$

(44) is true for $b = 1$, by the definition (43). We assume it to be true for $b = k$, i.e.

$$(-a)k = -(ak) \tag{44'}$$

Then for $b = k+1$ we have, by (43), (44′), and (40)

$$(-a)(k+1) = (-a)k+(-a) = -(ak)-a$$
$$= -(ak+a) = -(a(k+1))$$

Hence (44) is indeed valid for all natural numbers b.

For $x = 0$ we have in particular

$$0 \cdot b = 0 \tag{45}$$

as can be shown at once by induction from (43).

The method of definition by induction according to (43) reduces multiplication to a repeated addition. In the form in which it is stated it can also be used for negative numbers x. However it cannot be used as it stands when the second factor is negative. In this case one can, of course, easily postulate the validity of the commutative law $xy = yx$. But it is more 'natural', as in the case of addition, to give a recursive definition, whereby multiplication by a negative second factor is defined by reference to its predecessor.[1]

$$x \cdot 1 = x$$

$$x \cdot {}'y = xy + (-x) = xy - x \qquad (46)$$

One can see at once that this law is valid (according to the definition (43)) for positive integers $y = b$. For $y = 1$ we have in particular

$$x \cdot 0 = x \cdot {}'1 = x \cdot 1 - x = x - x = 0 \qquad (46')$$

Further

$$x(-1) = x \cdot {}'0 = x \cdot 0 - x = 0 - x = -x$$

$$x(-2) = x \cdot {}'(-1) = x \cdot (-1) - x = -(x+x) = -(2x) \quad (46'')$$

$$x(-3) = x \cdot {}'(-2) = x \cdot (-2) - x = -(2x+x) = -(3x)$$

$$\cdots\cdots\cdots\cdots\cdots\cdots\cdots\cdots\cdots\cdots\cdots\cdots\cdots\cdots\cdots\cdots$$

By the principle of induction one can easily show that for positive integers a and b

$$a(-b) = -(ab) \qquad (47)$$

and

$$(-a)(-b) = ab \qquad (48)$$

We shall give the proof only for (48). For $b = 1$ we have by (46)

$$(-a)(-1) = (-a) \cdot {}'0 = (-a) \cdot 0 + (-(-a))$$

Hence by (39) we have

$$(-a)(-1) = a$$

If we now assume as induction hypothesis that

$$(-a)(-k) = ak$$

[1] See the definition (29) for addition.

then it follows from (46) that

$$(-a)(-(k+1)) = (-a).'(-k) = (-a)(-k) - (-a) = ak + a = a(k+1)$$

Thus (48) holds for all natural numbers b.

From (44), (47), and (48) it can easily be shown that (9), (10), (11), and (12) hold for arbitrary *integers*.

6. Definition of rational numbers

The 'inverse problem' for multiplication can be formulated as follows:

Given two integers x and y, find an integer z which satisfies the equation

$$x.z = y \qquad (49)$$

Obviously this equation does not have an integer solution z for every pair of numbers x and y. The equation $5z = 14$ is a counter example.

We have seen that the inverse problem of addition cannot always be solved in the domain of natural numbers (III 4) but only in the set Z of integers. This suggests the definition of a more extensive set of numbers Q, containing Z, in which the inverse problem for multiplication can be solved. In this set Q the operations of addition, subtraction and multiplication must be defined in such a way that the known rules for calculation (*e.g.*, (4), (5), (6), (9), (10), (11), (12)) are valid.

We shall try to find the properties which such a set Q ought to have.[1]

We first note that because

$$1.y = y \qquad (50)$$

all integers y must belong to Q. For by (50) $z = y$ is a solution of the equation $1.z = y$.

But let us now examine the equation

$$0.z = y \qquad (51)$$

We have

$$0.z = (x-x)z = xz - xz = 0$$

---

[1] In the following the elements of the set Q are denoted by p, q, r, s. The letters z, y, x, u denote integers, and a, b, c, d denote natural numbers.

Thus if $y \neq 0$, (51) is not soluble. On the other hand if $y = 0$, the equation $0 \cdot z = 0$ holds for all integers z.

In an attempt to solve the equation (49) for z we must, therefore, exclude the case $x = 0$. But we shall see that for all integers $x \neq 0$ and for arbitrary $y \in Z$ this problem has a unique solution in a suitable set Q.

Since equation (49) cannot always be solved by a number $z \in Z$, we shall write it in the following form

$$x \cdot p = y \tag{49'}$$

where p is an element of the set Q still to be defined. This 'number' p is evidently determined by the pair of integers y and x.

We shall now examine more closely the properties of such number pairs belonging to an equation (49'). We multiply the equation by an integer z and obtain

$$(zx)p = (zy) \tag{52}$$

always with the proviso that all the 'usual' rules of calculation hold for the number p. Thus p also satisfies the equation

$$u \cdot p = v \tag{53}$$

where

$$u = zx, \qquad v = zy \tag{54}$$

From (54) one obtains the relation

$$u \cdot y = v \cdot x \tag{55}$$

between the numbers x, y and u, v.

If two number pairs y/x and v/u ($x \neq 0$, $u \neq 0$) satisfy the relation (55), we shall call them *equivalent* (written $\approx$). Hence

$$(y/x \approx v/u) \Leftrightarrow (x \neq 0 \wedge u \neq 0 \wedge uy = vx) \tag{56}$$

Clearly for the equivalence relation defined in this way

$$(y/x \approx v/u) \Leftrightarrow (v/u \approx y/x) \tag{57}$$

$$y/x \approx y/x \tag{58}$$

$$(y_1/x_1 \approx y_2/x_2) \wedge (y_2/x_2 \approx y_3/x_3) \Rightarrow (y_1/x_1 \approx y_3/x_3) \tag{59}$$

Further, it follows from (54) that

$$y/x \approx zy/zx \tag{60}$$

for all integers $z \neq 0$.

A set of number pairs y/x which are equivalent in the sense of the definition (56) is called an *equivalence class* (a class of equivalent pairs) or a *rational number*.

The set Q of rational numbers is accordingly the set of all equivalence classes.

We denote such an equivalence class by $\{y/x\}$, where y/x is a pair of this class. If $y/x \approx v/u$, then both pairs determine the same class and hence the same rational number. Thus we have

$$y/x \approx v/u$$

but

$$p = \{y/x\} = \{v/u\} = \frac{y}{x} = \frac{v}{u}$$

Hence we write the 'fraction'[1] $\dfrac{y}{x} = \dfrac{v}{u}$ for the rational number which is given by the class of pairs equivalent to y/x. Thus, for example

$$\{2/3\} = \{-4/-6\} = \frac{2}{3} = \frac{-4}{-6}$$

The statement (60) can be interpreted as a rule for the 'cancelling' of fractions, viz.

$$\frac{y}{x} = \frac{zy}{zx} \tag{60'}$$

7. Calculation with rational numbers

There is nothing to prevent us from calling a set of equivalent number pairs a (rational) *number*. Nevertheless we wish to give a justification for this terminology. It is not usual to call any arbitrary set of things a *number*, and the beginner may surely maintain that a *set of number pairs* is something different from a number. One is accustomed to calculating with numbers, to adding them, multiplying them, and so on. We shall introduce for the newly-defined 'rational numbers' corresponding calculation processes and in so doing justify the terminology we have chosen.

[1] A fraction is a rational number represented in the form $\dfrac{y}{x}$.

To do this we begin with the 'defining equation'

$$zp = y, \qquad xq = u \tag{61}$$

for the rational number

$$p = y/z = \frac{y}{z} \quad \text{and} \quad q = u/x = \frac{u}{x}$$

We assume first that it is permissible to calculate with rational numbers p and q according to the usual rules. We multiply the first of the equations (61) by x, the second by z, and add

$$(xz)p + (xz)q = xy + zu$$

or

$$xz(p+q) = xy + zu$$

Hence $p+q$ is the rational number

$$p+q = \frac{xy+zu}{xz} \tag{62}$$

But one can also represent the numbers p and q by other pairs from the same equivalence classes, for example

$$p = \{y^*/z^*\}, \qquad q = \{u^*/x^*\} \tag{63}$$

We then have

$$y^*/z^* \approx y/z, \qquad u^*/x^* \approx u/x$$

and thus

$$y^*z = z^*y, \qquad u^*x = x^*u \tag{64}$$

For $p+q$ we obtain analogously with (62)

$$p+q = \frac{x^*y^* + z^*u^*}{x^*z^*} \tag{62'}$$

As can easily be checked the number pairs given by (62) and (62′) are equivalent, *i.e.*

$$xy+zu/xz \approx x^*y^* + z^*u^*/x^*z^* \tag{65}$$

This means: if we take any two number pairs which belong to the equivalence classes $p = \{y/z\}$ and $q = \{u/x\}$ respectively, then the number pairs $xy+zu/xz$ and $x^*y^* + z^*u^*/x^*z^*$ are elements of *one* equivalence class which we can denote by

$$xy + zu/xz = \frac{xy + zu}{xz}$$

This justifies the definition:

The sum $p+q$ of two rational numbers $p = \{y/z\}$, $q = \{u/x\}$ is given by (62).

In the special case $z = x = 1$ in the two equations (61) we have the integers y and u as solutions. Written as number pairs the solutions are $y/1$ and $u/1$. Accordingly we shall write

$$\frac{y}{1} = y, \qquad \frac{u}{1} = u \qquad (66)$$

For the sum of these two numbers we obtain by (62)

$$y + u = \frac{y + u}{1} \qquad (67)$$

There were good reasons for not admitting number pairs of the type $y/0$. However the case $y = 0$, $z \neq 0$ need not be excluded. By (51) we obtain

$$\frac{0}{1} = \frac{0}{2} = \ldots = 0 \qquad (68)$$

and

$$0 + \frac{a}{b} = \frac{0}{b} + \frac{a}{b} = \frac{a}{b} \qquad (69)$$

By (60') we have further

$$\frac{y}{z} = \frac{-y}{-z} \qquad (60'')$$

Hence we can express every rational number $p = \{y/z\}$ in such a way that the second number z is *positive*, viz.

$$p = \frac{y}{a} \qquad (70)$$

We then define

$$-p = -\frac{y}{a} = \frac{-y}{a} \qquad (71)$$

In this way we can define the difference of two rational numbers p and q simply by

$$p - q = p + (-q) \tag{72}$$

A fraction in the 'standard form' (70) is called *positive* if y is positive. This makes it possible to introduce an ordering for rational numbers. We have

$$p = \frac{y}{a} < q = \frac{z}{b}$$

whenever the difference

$$q - p = \frac{za - yb}{ab}$$

is positive.

With the assumptions about a and b this will be the case if, and only if, $za > yb$. One can easily show that for the ordering defined in this way the theorems O_1 and O_2 of II 7 are valid. By (66) this new ordering is in agreement with the ordering introduced earlier.

To define *multiplication* of rational numbers we go back again to the defining equation (61). We first assume that formal multiplication obeying the usual rules is possible with rational numbers. We can then multiply the left hand sides and the right hand sides of the two equations (61) and obtain

$$(zx) \cdot (pq) = yu$$

This suggests defining the product of the fractions

$$p = \frac{y}{z} \quad \text{and} \quad q = \frac{u}{x}$$

by

$$pq = \frac{yu}{zx} \tag{73}$$

We can easily convince ourselves that to the equivalent pairs y/z and y^*/z^*, u/x and u^*/x^* respectively also belongs an equivalent 'product pair'

$$yu/zx \approx y^*u^*/z^*x^*$$

It is further readily seen that for integers $p = y$ and $q = u$ the new definition of multiplication (for the corresponding pairs $z/1$ and $u/1$) is in agreement with the already known one. For we have

$$\frac{y}{1} \cdot \frac{u}{1} = \frac{y \cdot u}{1} = y \cdot u$$

We omit the proof that for multiplication so defined the associative, commutative, and distributive laws hold and shall deal only with the question of the inverse of multiplication (*i.e.* 'division').

This question can at once be settled for arbitrary rational numbers p and q ($p \neq 0$). The equation

$$pr = q \qquad \left(p = \frac{y}{a}, q = \frac{u}{b} \right) \tag{74}$$

for $p \neq 0$ clearly has the solution

$$r = \frac{u}{b} \cdot \frac{a}{y} = \frac{u \cdot a}{b \cdot y}$$

In fact, by (60′) and the associative and commutative laws for the multiplication of integers we have

$$p \cdot r = \frac{y}{a} \cdot \frac{u \cdot a}{b \cdot y} = \frac{u(ay)}{b(ay)} = \frac{u}{b} = q$$

Hence *for any two rational numbers*

$$p = \frac{y}{a}, \qquad q = \frac{u}{b}$$

there exists, when $p \neq 0$ a well-defined number[1]

$$r = \frac{q}{p} = \frac{ua}{by}$$

for which $p.r = q$.

r is called the *quotient* of p and q.

To summarize: *for any two numbers p and q in the set Q of rational numbers the sum $p+q$, the difference $p-q$ and the product pq are uniquely determined. For $p \neq 0$ there exists a well-defined quotient*

$r = \dfrac{q}{p},$ *which satisfies the equation*

$$r \cdot p = q$$

---

[1] The proof of the uniqueness of division is left to the reader.

We have already, several times, used the term 'equivalent' for a relation. We called two sets of the same cardinal number *equivalent* (p. 34) and in this chapter we introduced the equivalence of pairs of integers.

In general we call a relation $\sim$ between the elements of a set M a (binary) *equivalence relation* if it has the following properties

$$a \sim b \Leftrightarrow b \sim a, \qquad a \sim a$$

$$[(a \sim b) \wedge (b \sim c)] \Rightarrow (a \sim c) \tag{75}$$

Clearly the equivalence of number pairs denoted by the symbol $\approx$ has the properties (75). They also hold, for example, for the congruence of segments and angles or the similarity of triangles in geometry. It does not depend on the symbol used (for instance $\equiv$ for the congruence of segments) but on the validity of the propositions (75).

8. Problems

1. Prove (5) using the principle of induction.
2. Using the definition (8) prove that $2 \cdot 2 = 4$, where $4 = ||||| = 0''''$ $= 1'''$.
3. Prove (10) using the principle of induction.
4. Prove the 'little Fermat theorem'. For all prime numbers[1] p and for all natural numbers n, p is a divisor of $n^p - n$.
5. Show that for all natural numbers n, $n^3 - n$ is divisible by 6.
6. The number pairs[2] (x, y), where x and y are integers, can be ordered by the rule

$$(x, y) \prec (x_1, y_1)$$

if the first of the differences

$$x_1 - x, \qquad y_1 - y$$

which does not vanish is *positive*.
Is this ordering a well-ordering?
7. Show that the ordering of the positive rational numbers is *archimedean*. This means that for any two numbers $p \in Q$, $q \in Q$

---

[1] A natural number p is called a *prime number* if 1 and p are its only divisors.
[2] One can also order complex numbers $x + iy$, where x and y are integers, by this definition.

$(p = a/b, q = c/d)$ there exists a natural number n such that $n \cdot p > q$.

8. For the number pairs (x, y) defined in problem (6) one can define an addition by

$$(x, y) + (u, v) = (x + u, y + v)$$

Multiplication by a natural number n is then given by

$$n \cdot (x, y) = (n \cdot x, n \cdot y)$$

Show that the ordering of number pairs defined in problem (6) is *not archimedean*.

CHAPTER FOUR

Groups

1. Symmetries of the tetrahedron

The regular tetrahedron of Fig. 13 with vertices 1, 2, 3, 4 possesses a number of symmetry properties. The configuration can be brought into coincidence with itself by rotation through 0°, 120°, or 240° about the altitude through vertex 1. The vertex 1 remains fixed. A

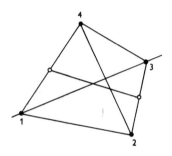

FIG. 13.

rotation through 120° (and of appropriate sense) gives for the remaining vertices the mapping

$$2 \to 3, \quad 3 \to 4, \quad 4 \to 2$$

whilst for a rotation through 240° we obtain

$$2 \to 4, \quad 3 \to 2, \quad 4 \to 3$$

and again obviously $1 \to 1$.

Such a mapping of a finite set[1] onto itself is called a *permutation*.

[1] In this case the mapping of the four numbers 1, 2, 3, 4.

The three permutations corresponding to the three rotations can also be represented in the form

$$s_1 = \begin{pmatrix} 1 & 2 & 3 & 4 \\ 1 & 2 & 3 & 4 \end{pmatrix}, \quad s_2 = \begin{pmatrix} 1 & 2 & 3 & 4 \\ 1 & 3 & 4 & 2 \end{pmatrix}$$

$$s_3 = \begin{pmatrix} 1 & 2 & 3 & 4 \\ 1 & 4 & 2 & 3 \end{pmatrix}$$

where in each case a number in the top line is mapped into the number below it.[1]

Naturally, instead of keeping the vertex 1 fixed, one can fix any of the remaining vertices. This gives $3 . 2 = 6$ further permutations[2]

$$s_4 = \begin{pmatrix} 1 & 2 & 3 & 4 \\ 3 & 2 & 4 & 1 \end{pmatrix}, \quad s_5 = \begin{pmatrix} 1 & 2 & 3 & 4 \\ 4 & 2 & 1 & 3 \end{pmatrix}$$

$$s_6 = \begin{pmatrix} 1 & 2 & 3 & 4 \\ 2 & 4 & 3 & 1 \end{pmatrix}, \quad s_7 = \begin{pmatrix} 1 & 2 & 3 & 4 \\ 4 & 1 & 3 & 2 \end{pmatrix}$$

$$s_8 = \begin{pmatrix} 1 & 2 & 3 & 4 \\ 2 & 3 & 1 & 4 \end{pmatrix}, \quad s_9 = \begin{pmatrix} 1 & 2 & 3 & 4 \\ 3 & 1 & 2 & 4 \end{pmatrix}$$

Finally one can also rotate the tetrahedron about a line joining the mid points of opposite edges. For example a rotation through 180° about the line through the mid points of $\overline{1,4}$ and $\overline{2,3}$ (see Fig. 13) again brings the tetrahedron into coincidence with itself and gives the permutation

$$s_{10} = \begin{pmatrix} 1 & 2 & 3 & 4 \\ 4 & 3 & 2 & 1 \end{pmatrix}$$

The corresponding permutations for the remaining two possible axes are

$$s_{11} = \begin{pmatrix} 1 & 2 & 3 & 4 \\ 2 & 1 & 4 & 3 \end{pmatrix}, \quad s_{12} = \begin{pmatrix} 1 & 2 & 3 & 4 \\ 3 & 4 & 1 & 2 \end{pmatrix}$$

[1] We generally write the numbers in the top line of a permutation in natural order, but one does not alter the mapping if one permutes the numbers in the top line and applies the same permutation to the numbers in the second line. For example

$$s_2 = \begin{pmatrix} 3 & 1 & 2 & 4 \\ 4 & 1 & 3 & 2 \end{pmatrix} = \begin{pmatrix} 4 & 3 & 2 & 1 \\ 2 & 4 & 3 & 1 \end{pmatrix}$$

[2] We do not count the rotation through 0° again. It is already given by the permutation s_1.

We shall now examine what the resulting permutation is when *two permutations s_n ($n = 1, 2, 3, \ldots, 12$) are performed one after the other.* For example, if we carry out the rotations s_3 and s_5 one after the other, then we have to perform the following mapping of the four numbers 1, 2, 3, 4

$$
\begin{array}{ccc}
s_3 & s_5 & \\
1 \to 1 \to 4 & & \\
2 \to 4 \to 3 & & (1) \\
3 \to 2 \to 2 & & \\
4 \to 3 \to 1 & &
\end{array}
$$

We shall denote the permutation which results from the "combination" of the permutations s_3 and s_5 by $s_3 \circ s_5$. From (1) we have

$$
s_3 \circ s_5 = s_{10} = \begin{pmatrix} 1 & 2 & 3 & 4 \\ 4 & 3 & 2 & 1 \end{pmatrix} \tag{2}
$$

This result can be interpreted as follows. The result of turning the tetrahedron about the vertices 1 and 2 through $240°$ in each case (in the given sense) is the same as turning it through $180°$ about an axis through the mid points of $\overline{1, 4}$ and $\overline{2, 3}$.

The law (2) has a formal resemblance to multiplication. One often denotes a combination of permutations as a product $s_3 s_5$ (without the symbol $\circ$). We shall retain the symbol $\circ$ to characterize the combination but shall call it a product.

In general the product does not satisfy the commutative law. For example, it is easily checked that

$$
s_5 \circ s_3 = s_{12} = \begin{pmatrix} 1 & 2 & 3 & 4 \\ 3 & 4 & 1 & 2 \end{pmatrix}, \qquad s_3 \circ s_5 = s_{10}
$$

If one determines all possible products $s_\mu \circ s_\nu$ ($\mu = 1, 2, \ldots, 12$, $\nu = 1, 2, \ldots, 12$) one finds that all the 144 products agree with one or other of the permutations $s_1, s_2, \ldots, s_{12}$. This can be expressed as follows:

The product of any two elements of the set

$$
G_1 = \{s_1, s_2, s_3, \ldots, s_{12}\} \tag{3}
$$

is again an element of G_1.

This is by no means obvious. If we had confined ourselves to the permutations $s_1, s_2, s_3, \ldots, s_9$ and omitted the three rotations through $180°$, then it would not have been possible to obtain such a closure property for the subset $G_1^* \subset G_1$. For we have, as already shown, $s_3 \circ s_5 = s_{10}$ and this permutation does not belong to the set $G_1^* = \{s_1, s_2, \ldots, s_9\}$.

We now arrange all 144 products $s_\mu \circ s_\nu$ in the form of a table.

Table 1. (G_1)

	s_ν											
	1	2	3	4	5	6	7	8	9	10	11	12
1	1	2	3	4	5	6	7	8	9	10	11	12
2	2	3	1	12	7	8	10	11	4	5	6	9
3	3	1	2	9	10	11	5	6	12	7	8	4
4	4	10	6	5	1	12	9	2	11	8	7	3
5	5	8	12	1	4	3	11	10	7	2	9	6
6	6	4	10	11	8	7	1	12	3	9	2	5
7	7	11	9	2	12	1	6	5	10	3	4	8
8	8	12	5	6	11	10	2	9	1	4	3	7
9	9	7	11	10	3	4	12	1	8	6	5	2
10	10	6	4	3	9	2	8	7	5	1	12	11
11	11	9	7	8	6	5	3	4	2	12	1	10
12	12	5	8	7	2	9	4	3	6	11	10	1

(The left margin is labelled s_μ.)

This table has a remarkable property. In *every* row and in *every* column each of the numbers $1, 2, 3, \ldots, 12$ occurs exactly once. It is thus possible to solve the 'inverse problem'. Given the permutations s_μ and s_ν we seek a permutation s_x which satisfies the equation

$$s_\mu \circ s_x = s_\nu$$

The solution can, in every case, be obtained from the table. For example, the equation $s_3 \circ s_x = s_7$ has the solution $s_x = s_{10}$, as can be seen from the third row of the table. For $s_y \circ s_3 = s_7$ one finds from the third column $s_y = s_{11}$.

2. Permutations

The above 12 permutations s_n which are determined by the symmetry properties of the tetrahedron form only a subset of all the permutations which are possible for the four elements 1, 2, 3, 4. In fact the number of ways $A(n)$ of arranging n elements in order is

$$A(n) = n! = 1 \cdot 2 \cdot 3 \ldots n \qquad (4)$$

This can easily be proved by mathematical induction. Thus there are $4! = 24$ possible permutations of the type

$$s = \begin{pmatrix} 1 & 2 & 3 & 4 \\ n_1 & n_2 & n_3 & n_4 \end{pmatrix} \qquad (5)$$

where n_1, n_2, n_3, n_4 stands for an arbitrary arrangement of the numbers 1, 2, 3, 4. In IV 1 we were concerned with only 12 of the 24 permutations of the type (5). These did not include, for example, the permutations

$$\begin{pmatrix} 1 & 2 & 3 & 4 \\ 4 & 3 & 1 & 2 \end{pmatrix} \quad \text{and} \quad \begin{pmatrix} 1 & 2 & 3 & 4 \\ 2 & 3 & 4 & 1 \end{pmatrix}$$

It is clear that any two permutations of n elements performed one after the other will again give such a permutation. Thus the set of all permutations of n elements shows a similar closure property to the subset considered in IV 1 (for $n = 4$).

It is thus possible to combine all the 24 permutations of 4 elements 1, 2, 3, 4 by forming the 'product' ∘ and arrange the $24 \cdot 24 = 576$ possible products in a scheme corresponding to Table 1.

We shall now collect together some of the properties of the permutations

$$s = \begin{pmatrix} 1 & 2 & 3 & \ldots & n \\ m_1 & m_2 & m_3 & \ldots & m_n \end{pmatrix}$$

of n elements.[1]

(E_1) *The combination of permutations is associative.*[2]

$$s \circ (t \circ r) = (s \circ t) \circ r \qquad (6)$$

---

[1] n is called the *degree* of the permutation.
[2] All the permutations to be combined are of the same degree.

To show this we assume that the permutation s associates with the natural number $\sigma\,(1 \leqslant \sigma \leqslant n)$ the number τ

$$s = \begin{pmatrix} \cdots & \sigma & \cdots \\ \cdots & \tau & \cdots \end{pmatrix}$$

The number τ must then occur in the top row of the permutation t. Let

$$t = \begin{pmatrix} \cdots & \tau & \cdots \\ \cdots & \rho & \cdots \end{pmatrix}$$

and finally

$$r = \begin{pmatrix} \cdots & \rho & \cdots \\ \cdots & \nu & \cdots \end{pmatrix}$$

Then clearly

$$s \circ (t \circ r) = (s \circ t) \circ r = \begin{pmatrix} \cdots & \sigma & \cdots \\ \cdots & \nu & \cdots \end{pmatrix} \tag{7}$$

$(\boldsymbol{E_2})$ *For every permutation s there exists an inverse permutation s^{-1}, such that*

$$s \circ s^{-1} = e \tag{8}$$

where e stands for the identity

$$e = \begin{pmatrix} 1 & 2 & 3 & \cdots & n \\ 1 & 2 & 3 & \cdots & n \end{pmatrix}$$

To prove (8) we have only to associate with the permutation

$$s = \begin{pmatrix} 1 & 2 & 3 & \cdots & n \\ m_1 & m_2 & m_3 & \cdots & m_n \end{pmatrix}$$

the permutation

$$t = \begin{pmatrix} m_1 & m_2 & m_3 & \cdots & m_n \\ 1 & 2 & 3 & \cdots & n \end{pmatrix} \tag{9}$$

We now arrange the numbers of the top row of (9) in the natural order $1, 2, 3, \ldots, n$ and move with each number m_ν of this row the number below it. t then takes the 'normal form'

$$t = \begin{pmatrix} 1 & 2 & 3 & \ldots & n \\ t_1 & t_2 & t_3 & \ldots & t_n \end{pmatrix} \tag{9'}$$

where t_v is the natural number that stands below $m_\rho = v$ in (9).

Clearly for the permutation t

$$t \circ s = s \circ t = e$$

Thus $t = s^{-1}$.

The 'powers' of a permutation are defined by

$$s^0 = e, s^1 = s, s^2 = s \circ s, \ldots, s^{k+1} = s^k \circ s;$$

$$s^{-2} = s^{-1} \circ s^{-1}, \ldots, s^{-k-1} = s^{-k} \circ s^{-1}$$

We note that for all integers m and n these powers obey the rules

(E_3) $\qquad s^m \circ s^n = s^{m+n}, \qquad (s^m)^n = s^{m.n}$

These can easily be proved by induction from the defining equations.

For every permutation s (of degree n) there must exist a natural number k such that $s^k = e$. For the powers

$$s, s^2, s^3, s^4, \ldots$$

cannot all be different, since there are only $n!$ permutations of degree n. Let $s^\rho = s^\sigma$ say, with $\rho - \sigma = k$. It then follows from (E_3) that

$$s^{\rho - \sigma} = s^k = s^{\sigma - \rho} = s^0 = e$$

The smallest number k for which $s^k = e$ is called the *order* of the permutation s.

Permutations of the type

$$z = \begin{pmatrix} a_1 & a_2 & a_3 & \ldots & a_{n-1} & a_n \\ a_2 & a_3 & a_4 & \ldots & a_n & a_1 \end{pmatrix} \tag{10}$$

are called *cycles*. The functional correspondence of this permutation can best be illustrated by the 'cyclic' arrangement of the elements, which for $n = 5$ is shown in Fig. 14.

For convenience in printing we replace the representation of (10) or of Fig. 14 by a simple bracket

$$z = (a_1 \quad a_2 \quad a_3 \quad \ldots \quad a_n) \tag{10'}$$

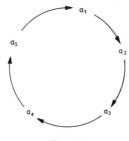

FIG. 14

Not every permutation is a cycle, but every permutation can be resolved into a certain number of cycles. To do this we select an arbitrary element a_1 from the top row of s. Let it correspond to the number a_2. To a_2 let s assign the image a_3, to a_3, a_4 and so on. After a finite number of steps we arrive at the image a_1, since the number a_1 must also occur in the second row of s. Hence we have found *one* cycle in s. If s is not exhausted, we can find further cycles in the same way. A number which is mapped onto itself is considered as a cycle with one member. Consider an example. The permutation

$$s = \begin{pmatrix} 1 & 2 & 3 & 4 & 5 & 6 & 7 & 8 & 9 \\ 3 & 5 & 9 & 4 & 7 & 1 & 2 & 8 & 6 \end{pmatrix}$$

contains the two cyclic interchanges (1 3 9 6) and (2 5 7). 4 and 8 are replaced by themselves and thus represent one member cycles. We therefore have

$$s = (1 \ 3 \ 9 \ 6) \ (2 \ 5 \ 7) \ (4) \ (8)$$

The permutations considered in IV 1 in connection with the symmetries of the tetrahedron can be resolved into cycles as follows

$$s_1 = (1) \ (2) \ (3) \ (4), \qquad s_2 = (2 \ 3 \ 4) \ (1)$$
$$s_3 = (2 \ 4 \ 3) \ (1) \quad \text{etc.}$$

The last three permutations are of a different type; they consist of two-term cycles, *e.g.*

$$s_{10} = (1 \ 4) \ (2 \ 3)$$

For a cycle z the product table $z^\rho \circ z^\sigma$ assumes a particularly simple form. For example, let

$$z = (1 \ 2 \ 3 \ 4 \ 5 \ 6)$$

and let G_2 be the set of permutations $\{s_1 = e, s_2 = z, s_3 = z^2, \ldots$ $s_6 = z^5\}$. For the suffixes of $s_\rho = s_\chi \circ s_\lambda$ we then obtain the table

Table 2. (G_2)

	s_λ					
	1	2	3	4	5	6
1	1	2	3	4	5	6
2	2	3	4	5	6	1
s_χ 3	3	4	5	6	1	2
4	4	5	6	1	2	3
5	5	6	1	2	3	4
6	6	1	2	3	4	5

3. Definition of a group

Let us now consider the properties of the set G_3 of functions

$$f_1(x) = x, \quad f_2(x) = \frac{1}{x}, \quad f_3(x) = 1-x$$

$$f_4(x) = \frac{x}{-1+x}, \quad f_5(x) = \frac{1}{1-x}, \quad f_6(x) = 1 - \frac{1}{x}$$

Of special interest are the regularities that are revealed when functions from the set G_3 are combined. For example

$$f_2(f_3(x)) = \frac{1}{1-x} = f_5(x), \qquad f_3(f_2(x)) = 1 - \frac{1}{x} = f_6(x)$$

Using the abbreviation $f_\nu \circ f_\mu$ for the function $f_\nu(f_\mu(x))$, then

$$f_2 \circ f_3 = f_5, \qquad f_3 \circ f_2 = f_6$$

It is not difficult to form all the 36 'products' $f_\nu \circ f_\mu$ and this would again show that for the set G_3 *all products $f_\nu \circ f_\mu$ belong to* G_3. We thus obtain for the combination of the functions, or for the products $f_\nu \circ f_\mu$ the table

Table 3. (G_3)

		f_μ				
	1	2	3	4	5	6
1	1	2	3	4	5	6
2	2	1	5	6	3	4
3	3	6	1	5	4	2
4	4	5	6	1	2	3
5	5	4	2	3	6	1
6	6	3	4	2	1	5

(The row labels are indexed by f_ν.)

The elements of the sets G_1 and G_2 (IV 1, 2) were *permutations*, and the elements of G_3 are the *functions* $f_\nu(x)$ ($\nu = 1, 2, 3, \ldots, 6$) *defined for all real numbers* x. The combination rule denoted by ° has for G_3 formally a different meaning from that for the sets G_1 and G_2. Nevertheless there are certain features common to the three sets and the combining of their elements by the symbol °, which leads to the following definition:

A set G is called a group if a combining operation (written °) *for its elements is defined such that the following postulates are satisfied:*

(G_1) *If s and t are two (identical or different) elements of G, then s ° t is also an element of G.*

(G_2) *The operation is associative, i.e.,* $s ° (t ° u) = (s ° t) ° u$.

(G_3) *There exists an 'identity element' e for which* $s ° e = e ° s = s$ *for all* $s \in G$.

(G_4) *For each element* $g \in G$ *there exists an element* $g^{-1} \in G$ *such that* $g ° g^{-1} = e$.

One can see at once that the sets G_1, G_2, and G_3 considered so far have the character of groups. We have already shown that the permutations of the sets G_1 and G_2 have the properties (G_1) to (G_4). One can easily see from Table 3 that the last defined function set G_3 also satisfies the four postulates. The identity element for G_1 and G_2 is the permutation s_1, and for the set G_3 it is the function $f_1(x) = x$.

We have introduced the neutral symbol ° for the combining operation in the group. This may be replaced, from time to time, by another symbol, provided that the group postulates are satisfied for this symbol.

We shall now give some examples to illustrate the wide range of application of the group concept.

(I). *The set Z of integers forms a group with respect to the operation expressed by the symbol +. The identity element is the number 0.*

(G_1) is satisfied, for if $u \in Z$ and $v \in Z$ then $u + v \in Z$. We have already noted the associative law for addition in Chapter II. The number 0 has indeed the character of the identity element, since for all elements $z \in Z$ we have $z + 0 = 0 + z = z$. Finally (G_4) holds, for the number $(-z)$ is the inverse of z. We have $z + (-z) = 0$, and 0 is our identity element.

(II). The linear transformations

$$y_1 = a_{11}x_1 + a_{12}x_2$$
$$y_2 = a_{21}x_1 + a_{22}x_2 \tag{11}$$

with non-vanishing determinant

$$|\alpha| = \begin{vmatrix} a_{11} & a_{12} \\ a_{21} & a_{22} \end{vmatrix} = a_{11}a_{22} - a_{21}a_{12} \tag{11'}$$

and rational coefficients a_{ik} suggest the definition of a further group. To show this we 'combine' the transformation (11) with[1]

$$z_1 = b_{11}y_1 + b_{12}y_2$$
$$z_2 = b_{21}y_1 + b_{22}y_2 \tag{12}$$

This gives

$$z_1 = c_{11}x_1 + c_{12}x_2$$
$$z_2 = c_{21}x_1 + c_{22}x_2 \tag{13}$$

where

$$c_{11} = b_{11}a_{11} + b_{12}a_{21}, \qquad c_{12} = b_{11}a_{12} + b_{12}a_{22}$$
$$c_{21} = b_{21}a_{11} + b_{22}a_{21}, \qquad c_{22} = b_{21}a_{12} + b_{22}a_{22} \tag{14}$$

---

[1] For this transformation also the determinant is non-zero.

The transformations (11) and (12) are characterized by the matrices[1]

$$\alpha = \begin{pmatrix} a_{11} & a_{12} \\ a_{21} & a_{22} \end{pmatrix}, \qquad \beta = \begin{pmatrix} b_{11} & b_{12} \\ b_{21} & b_{22} \end{pmatrix} \qquad (15)$$

To the 'combined' transformation (13) belongs the corresponding matrix

$$\gamma = \begin{pmatrix} c_{11} & c_{12} \\ c_{21} & c_{22} \end{pmatrix}$$

We now call γ the *product* of the matrices β and α, i.e., $\gamma = \beta \circ \alpha$, where the elements of γ are given by (14).[2]

Thus to every transformation (11) we can assign uniquely a matrix. The combination of transformations with matrices β and α then gives rise to a transformation with matrix $\gamma = \beta \circ \alpha$.

We now show that *the matrices*

$$\alpha = \begin{pmatrix} a_{11} & a_{12} \\ a_{21} & a_{22} \end{pmatrix}$$

with non-vanishing determinants (11′) form a group G_4. *The product of two matrices* $\beta \circ \alpha = \gamma$ *is a matrix whose elements are given by* (14).

It is easy to show[3] that this multiplication is associative. Since the determinant of the product is also non-zero,[4] the group postulates (G_1) and (G_2) are satisfied. For the identity matrix

$$\varepsilon = \begin{pmatrix} 1 & 0 \\ 0 & 1 \end{pmatrix} \qquad (16)$$

[1] A matrix is a rectangular array of numbers. We have here the special case of a two-rowed square matrix.

[2] One obtains the elements of the matrix $\gamma = \beta \circ \alpha$ if one forms the *inner product*

$$\sum_{l=1}^{2} b_{il} a_{lk}$$

of the rows of β and the columns of α.

[3] This can be done using the definition of the matrices of our group G_4 given here. For the proof for arbitrary matrices see, *e.g.*, Feigl-Rohrbach.

[4] If $\beta \circ \alpha = \gamma$, then for the determinants also $|\beta| \cdot |\alpha| = |\gamma|$.

we clearly have $\alpha \circ \varepsilon = \varepsilon \circ \alpha = \alpha$ for all elements $\alpha \in G$. Finally the matrix[1]

$$\alpha^{-1} = \begin{pmatrix} \dfrac{a_{22}}{|\alpha|} & \dfrac{-a_{12}}{|\alpha|} \\[2ex] \dfrac{-a_{21}}{|\alpha|} & \dfrac{a_{11}}{|\alpha|} \end{pmatrix},$$

where

$$|\alpha| = \begin{vmatrix} a_{11} & a_{12} \\ a_{21} & a_{22} \end{vmatrix} = a_{11}a_{22} - a_{21}a_{12},$$

is the inverse of α. For $\alpha \circ \alpha^{-1} = \alpha^{-1} \circ \alpha = \varepsilon$, as one can easily show. The inner product of the i-th row ($i = 1, 2$) of α and the k-th column ($k = 1, 2$) of α^{-1} is

$$\delta_{ik} = \begin{cases} +1 & \text{for } i = k \\ 0 & \text{for } i \neq k \end{cases}$$

Hence G_4 satisfies all the group axioms. Since every matrix α corresponds to a linear transformation, and the multiplication of matrices can be associated with the 'combination' of the corresponding transformations, one can say also that the transformations (11) with non-vanishing determinant form a group. These transformations can be interpreted geometrically as projective mappings of a line onto itself.

(III). *The set of matrices* (15) *with determinant* $|\alpha| = 1$ *form a group* G_5, where $G_5 \subset G_4$. To show this one need only note that the identity matrix (16) belongs to G_5 and that the product of two matrices with determinants $|\alpha| = 1$ and $|\beta| = 1$ has again the determinant $|\alpha| \cdot |\beta| = 1$.

The transformations (15) corresponding to the matrices of the group G_5 can be interpreted as rotations of the rectangular co-ordinate system (x_1, x_2) into a corresponding system (y_1, y_2)[2] (see Fig. 15).

(IV). *The set* $G_6 = \{-1, +1\}$ *forms a group with respect to multiplication as the group operation.* The identity element is the

---

[1] At this point we make use of the condition $|\alpha| \neq 0$.

[2] The numbers a_{ik} can also be interpreted as trigonometric functions of the angle of rotation ϕ, see, *e.g.*, Feigl-Rohrbach, p. 230.

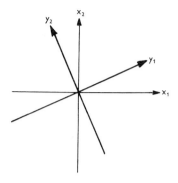

FIG. 15.

number 1. 1 has the order 1,[1] -1 the order 2, for $1^1 = 1$ and $(-1)^2 = 1$.

(V). Let G_7 be the set of all rational numbers with the exception of zero. G_7 *forms a group with respect to multiplication as the group operation.* The identity element is again the number 1. The number 0 must be excluded, since there is no rational number r for which $0 \cdot r = 1$. The number 1 again has the order 1, -1 has order 2, and for all the remaining numbers the order is infinite.

(VI). Let G_8 be the set of vectors in a plane E. G_8 *is a group with addition* (see Fig. 4b) *as operation.* The null-vector is the identity element, since for all vectors $g \in G$, $g + 0 = g$.

(VII). The regular hexagon of Fig. 16 is brought into coincidence with itself by a rotation of $k \cdot 60°$ ($k = 0, 1, 2, 3, 4, 5$) about its centre.

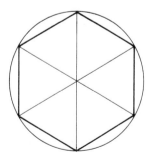

FIG. 16.

[1] See the definition on p. 74 for permutations. It can be applied to the elements of arbitrary groups. If, for an element a of a group, there exists no natural number n for which $a^n = e$, we say that a is of infinite order.

The simplest way to express these six rotations analytically is in the complex plane. Let the origin be the centre of the hexagon and the unit circle its circumscribed circle. The rotations can then be represented by

$$w_k = e^{i\pi k/3} \cdot z, \qquad k = 0, 1, 2, 3, 4, 5 \tag{17}$$

The multiplication $w_k \circ w_l$ is then defined by

$$w_k \circ w_l = w_{k+l}$$

where it is agreed that $w_{k+6} = w_k$.

These functions form a group G_9 with identity element $w_0 = z$.

The number of elements of a group is also called its *order*. Of the groups considered so far, G_1, G_2, G_3, G_6 and G_9 are *of finite order*, whereas Z, G_4, G_5, G_7 and G_8 are *of infinite order.*[1]

A group G is called an *Abelian group* if, for all $g, h \in G, g \circ h = h \circ g$. The reader should investigate which of the above groups satisfy this commutative law.

4. Properties of groups

As the examples of IV 3 show, the group postulates (G_1) to (G_4) can be satisfied by sets of very different types. Therein lies the fascination (and the practical importance) of modern mathematical structures. They reveal regularities which have applications in different fields of mathematics. General theorems on groups can be used in the theory of permutations and also, for example, in matrix algebra and geometrical transformations.

We shall derive below a few general theorems about groups from the postulates (G_1) to (G_4).

In every group there is only one identity element.

That there is *at least* one identity element in every group with the property $g \circ e = e \circ g = g$ (for all $g \in G$) is postulated by (G_3). We shall now show that there *cannot be more* than one identity element in G. If there were another identity element $e' \neq e$, then for all $g \in G$

$$g \circ e' = e' \circ g = g$$

In particular, for $g = e$ this gives

$$e \circ e' = e$$

---

[1] For short, one also speaks of finite and infinite groups.

By (G_3), for $s = e'$, we have further $e \circ e' = e'$, and from the last two equations we then obtain $e' = e$.

For the group G_1 we can always solve the inverse problem from the multiplication Table 1. We can show that this is possible for *every* group G. To do this we first prove that *to every element $g \in G$ there corresponds one, and only one, element $h = g^{-1} \in G$ such that*

$$h \circ g = g \circ h = e \qquad (18)$$

The emphasis here is on *one, and only one*. That there exists an element at all with the property (18) is postulated in (G_4). Let us assume that

$$g \circ h_1 = g \circ h_2 = e, \qquad h_1 \neq h_2 \qquad (19)$$

By (G_4) there exists an element $k \in G$ with the property

$$h_1 \circ k = e \qquad (20)$$

Then by (G_2), (19) and (20)

$$g \circ h_1 \circ k = \begin{cases} g \circ (h_1 \circ k) = g \circ e = g \\ (g \circ h_1) \circ k = e \circ k = k \end{cases}$$

and thus $g = k$. From this follows further that

$$h_1 = h_1 \circ e = h_1 \circ (g \circ h_2) = (h_1 \circ g) \circ h_2 = e \circ h_2 = h_2$$

This uniquely determined element $h_1 = h_2 = h \in G$ we shall denote by g^{-1}.

We can now show that:

For every group 'left hand' and 'right hand' division is possible in one, and only one, way.

This means that *for any two elements g and h of a group G there exist exactly one element x and one element y such that*

$$g \circ x = h, \qquad y \circ g = h \qquad (21)$$

Suppose elements x and y exist having the property (21). Then multiplication by g^{-1} gives

$$x = g^{-1} \circ h, \qquad y = h \circ g^{-1} \qquad (22)$$

Since g^{-1} (as already shown) is uniquely determined, then by (22) there *cannot be more than one* solution of the division problem. However, since multiplication of (22) by g again leads to (21), the group elements x and y given by (22) are, in fact, solutions of (21).

In general $x \neq y$, as has already been shown for the group G_1 in IV 1. For *abelian groups* we obviously have $x = y$.

If g is any fixed element of a group G, then $x \circ g$ and $g \circ y$ run through all the elements of G, if x and y do so.

As a result, every row and every column of a group table for a finite group of degree n contains each of the natural numbers $1, 2, 3, \ldots, n$ exactly once. We have noticed this already in Tables 1, 2, and 3.

To prove the theorem we note that, because of the uniqueness of division, $x' \circ g \neq x \circ g$ if $x \neq x'$. Hence if x runs through all the elements of the group, so also will $x \circ g$. Then

1) All $x \circ g$ are different.
2) All elements $h \in G$ do occur among the products $x \circ g = h$.

To justify 2) we have only to consider the equation $x \circ g = h$, which, according to the division theorem, has a unique solution. There exists, therefore, a well-defined element $x \in G$ for which $x \circ g = h.$[1]

Similarly one can prove the statement for y. From this follows, in particular, for the inverse element:

If g runs through all the elements of the group G, so also does g^{-1}.

To prepare the ground for a new concept we shall examine next the permutation group G_{10} of three elements $1, 2, 3$. It has $3! = 6$ elements which we shall denote as follows

$$s_1 = e = (1)\ (2)\ (3), \qquad s_2 = (1, 2)\ (3)$$

$$s_3 = (1, 3)\ (2), \qquad s_4 = (2, 3)\ (1)$$

$$s_5 = (1, 2, 3), \qquad s_6 = (1, 3, 2)$$

We now ask the reader to prepare a table of all possible products $s_\mu \circ s_\nu$ ($\mu = 1, 2, 3, \ldots, 6$, $\nu = 1, 2, 3, \ldots, 6$).[2] He will find that *the table of this group is identical with the table of the group G_3.* This means that if

$$s_\mu \circ s_\nu = s_\rho \qquad (s_\mu, s_\nu, s_\rho \in G_{10})$$

then also

$$f_\mu \circ f_\nu = f_\rho \qquad (f_\mu, f_\nu, f_\rho \in G_3)$$

Such a relationship does not exist between the groups G_3 and G_2. G_2 also has 6 elements, but the group table (Table 2) is different from those of G_3 and G_{10}.

---

[1] Note that for finite groups one can dispense with 2).

[2] This table is called the 'group table'.

Two groups G and G' are called isomorphic (written $G \cong G'$) *if there is a one-to-one correspondence*

$$g \leftrightarrow g', \, h \leftrightarrow h', \, k \leftrightarrow k', \ldots$$

between the elements $g, h, k, \ldots$ *of G and the elements* $g', h', k', \ldots$ *of G' which preserves products.*

This means that from $g \circ h = k$ it always follows that $g' \circ h' = k'$. For isomorphic groups with a finite or countable number of elements it is possible to arrange, by suitable numbering, that $g_v \leftrightarrow g'_v$ for all numbers v, and the statement concerning the products then takes the form

$$g_\mu \circ g_v = g_\rho \Leftrightarrow g'_\mu \circ g'_v = g'_\rho$$

Isomorphism between groups clearly has the character of *an equivalence relation*. This means that the relation is *reflexive, symmetric*, and *transitive, i.e.*

$$G \cong G \tag{23a}$$

$$(G \cong G') \Leftrightarrow (G' \cong G) \tag{23b}$$

$$[(G \cong G') \wedge (G' \cong G'')] \Rightarrow (G \cong G'') \tag{23c}$$

Thus the groups G_3 and G_{10} are isomorphic but the groups G_3 and G_2 are not. On the other hand $G_2 \cong G_9$, as one can easily show by forming the products.

To give an example of infinite isomorphic groups we define a set G_{11} by the powers 2^y, where y runs through the set Z of integers. G_{11} obviously forms a group under multiplication. From the equation

$$2^x \cdot 2^y = 2^{x+y}$$

one can see at once that G_{11} is isomorphic to the group Z of integers, in which the combining operation is addition.

Clearly isomorphisms are possible between very different types of sets. G_{10} is a set of permutations and the elements of G_3, on the other hand, are real functions. In G_{11} the group operation is multiplication whilst in Z, which is isomorphic to G_{11}, it is addition.

For finite groups, the concept of isomorphism makes it possible to confine the study of groups to the special case of permutation groups, for we have the theorem:

Every finite group G is isomorphic to a certain permutation group G', the degree of the permutation being equal to the order n of the group G.

This group G' is given by the n columns of the group table of G. To show this, we denote the elements of G by $g_1, g_2, g_3, \ldots, g_n$, and the indices of the products $g_\mu \circ g_\nu$ by μ/ν. Thus if

$$g_\mu \circ g_\nu = g_\rho$$

then we write $\mu|\nu$ for ρ. In the m-th column of the group table of G we then have the natural numbers

$$1|m, 2|m, 3|m, \ldots, n|m \tag{24}$$

where (24) is a permutation of the numbers $1, 2, 3, \ldots, n$. This follows from our general theorem about products in groups. The set G' of permutations is now defined by

$$s_m = \begin{pmatrix} 1 & 2 & 3 & \ldots & n \\ 1|m & 2|m & 3|m & \ldots & n|m \end{pmatrix}, \quad m = 1, 2, 3, \ldots, n$$

To show that G' possesses the required properties, we first form the products $g_\lambda \circ g_\mu \circ g_\nu$. By (G_2) and the definition of the symbol μ/ν we then have

$$g_{\lambda|(\mu|\nu)} = g_\lambda \circ g_{\mu|\nu} = g_\lambda \circ (g_\mu \circ g_\nu) = (g_\lambda \circ g_\mu) \circ g_\nu$$
$$= g_{(\lambda|\mu)} \circ g_\nu = g_{(\lambda|\mu)|\nu}.$$

Accordingly we obtain for the symbol $\mu|\nu$

$$\lambda|(\mu|\nu) = (\lambda|\mu)|\nu \tag{25}$$

Now with the product $g_\mu \circ g_\nu$ is associated the permutation

$$s_{\mu|\nu} = \begin{pmatrix} 1 & 2 & 3 & \ldots & n \\ 1|(\mu|\nu) & 2|(\mu|\nu) & 3|(\mu|\nu) & \ldots & n|(\mu|\nu) \end{pmatrix}$$

By (25) we can also write this

$$s_{\mu|\nu} = \begin{pmatrix} 1 & 2 & 3 & \ldots & n \\ (1|\mu)|\nu & (2|\mu)|\nu & (3|\mu)|\nu & \ldots & (n|\mu)|\nu \end{pmatrix} \tag{26}$$

Let us now examine the multiplication of the permutations themselves. We have

$$s_\mu \circ s_\nu = \begin{pmatrix} 1 & 2 & 3 & \dots & n \\ 1|\mu & 2|\mu & 3|\mu & \dots & n|\mu \end{pmatrix} \circ \begin{pmatrix} 1 & 2 & 3 & \dots & n \\ 1|\nu & 2|\nu & 3|\nu & \dots & n|\nu \end{pmatrix}$$

$$= s_\mu \circ \begin{pmatrix} 1|\mu & 2|\mu & \dots & n|\mu \\ (1|\mu)|\nu & (2|\mu)|\nu & \dots & (n|\mu)|\nu \end{pmatrix}$$

$$= \begin{pmatrix} 1 & 2 & \dots & n \\ (1|\mu)|\nu & (2|\mu)|\nu & \dots & (n|\mu)|\nu \end{pmatrix}$$

Thus by (26) we have in fact

$$s_\mu \circ s_\nu = s_{\mu|\nu}$$

Hence we have shown that the set G' of permutations is a group which is isomorphic to G.

5. Subgroups

As one can easily see from Table 1, the subsets

$$G_1^{(1)} = \{s_1, s_2, s_3\}$$
$$G_1^{(2)} = \{s_1, s_4, s_5\} \tag{27}$$
$$G_1^{(3)} = \{s_1, s_{10}, s_{11}, s_{12}\}$$

of the group G_1 themselves form groups. The product of any two elements of $G_1^{(1)}$, for example, is again an element of this subset. Since the identity element belongs to it and the remaining group postulates are also satisfied, we have indeed a subset of G_1 which is itself a group. The same holds for $G_1^{(2)}$ and $G_1^{(3)}$.

A subset $U \subset G$ which is itself a group is called a subgroup of G.

Of course not every arbitrary subset of a group has this property, even if the identity element belongs to it. We have already pointed out in IV 1 that the subset $\{s_1, s_2, \dots, s_9\}$ of G_1 is *not* a subgroup.

The non-empty subsets of a group (whether they are subgroups or not) are called *complexes*.

We shall first give some further examples of complexes which have the character of subgroups. The group G_1 is itself a subgroup of the group of *all* 24 permutations of the numbers 1, 2, 3, 4. Further (see IV 3) G_5 is a subgroup of G_4, G_6 a subgroup of G_7.

For a convenient formulation of additional propositions about complexes we introduce the concept of 'multiplication' of complexes. Let K and K' be arbitrary complexes of a group G. Then by $K \circ K'$ we shall understand the set of elements $k \circ k'$ with $k \in K$ and $k' \in K'$. Correspondingly we denote by $g \circ K$ the set of all products $g \circ k$ ($k \in K$), and finally $K \circ g$ stands for the set of all products $k \circ g$ ($k \in K$). g is a fixed element of G.

A complex K of a finite group G is a subgroup if, and only if,

$$K \circ K = K \tag{28}$$

This condition is obviously *necessary*. For if K is a subgroup, then a product of two elements of K must again belong to K. But (28) is also *sufficient* to ensure the group character of K. First, by (28), the group property (G_1) is satisfied. The associative law holds, since it holds for the whole group G. That the identity element also belongs to K follows from the fact that, by (28), with k all the powers k^m also belong to K. For some natural number n we must have $k^n = e$, since G is finite, by hypothesis. It follows that

$$k^{n-1} \circ k = k^n = e$$

so that $k^{n-1} = k^{-1}$. Hence k^{-1} also belongs to K and all the group postulates are satisfied.

We shall now determine the complexes $s_2 \circ G_1^{(3)}$ and $s_3 \circ G_1^{(3)}$ of the subgroup $G_1^{(3)}$ defined by (27). From Table 1 we find[1]

$$s_2 \circ G_1^{(3)} = \{s_2, s_5, s_6, s_9\}$$

$$s_3 \circ G_1^{(3)} = \{s_3, s_7, s_8, s_4\}$$

Accordingly every element of G_1 belongs to exactly one of the three complexes $G_1^{(3)}$, $s_2 \circ G_1^{(3)}$, $s_3 \circ G_1^{(3)}$. Hence the group can be represented as follows

$$G_1 = G_1^{(3)} \cup s_2 \circ G_1^{(3)} \cup s_3 \circ G_1^{(3)} \tag{29}$$

where the intersection of any two of the complexes on the right hand side is empty.

In the representation (29), s_2 can be replaced by any other element of the complex $s_2 \circ G_1^{(3)}$, and similarly s_3 by any element of the third complex. We have, as can be seen from Table 1

$$s_2 \circ G_1^{(3)} = s_5 \circ G_1^{(3)} = s_6 \circ G_1^{(3)} = s_9 \circ G_1^{(3)}$$

$$s_3 \circ G_1^{(3)} = s_7 \circ G_1^{(3)} = s_8 \circ G_1^{(3)} = s_4 \circ G_1^{(3)} \tag{30}$$

---

[1] Two sets are regarded as *equal* when they contain the same elements. The order of the elements in the enumeration is immaterial.

Hence by (30) we can also represent G_1 in the form

$$G_1 = G_1^{(3)} \cup s_5 \circ G_1^{(3)} \cup s_8 \circ G_1^{(3)} \qquad (29')$$

The complexes $s_v \circ G_1^{(3)}$ in the representations (29) and (29') are also called *left cosets* of the subgroup $G_1^{(3)}$ of G_1. A corresponding decomposition of G_1 into *right cosets* is possible

$$G_1 = G_1^{(3)} \cup G_1^{(3)} \circ s_2 \cup G_1^{(3)} \circ s_3 \qquad (31)$$

For both the subgroups $G_1^{(1)}$ and $G_1^{(2)}$ of (27) corresponding decompositions are possible. For $G_1^{(1)}$ the decomposition into left and right cosets is

$$G_1 = \begin{cases} G_1^{(1)} \cup s_4 \circ G_1^{(1)} \cup s_5 \circ G_1^{(1)} \cup s_7 \circ G_1^{(1)} \\ G_1^{(1)} \cup G_1^{(1)} \circ s_4 \cup G_1^{(1)} \circ s_5 \cup G_1^{(1)} \circ s_6 \end{cases} \qquad (32)$$

The above decompositions of a group into cosets of a subgroup are examples of a general theorem.

Let U be a subgroup of a finite group G of order n. The order m of the subgroup is then a divisor of n ($n = m \cdot r$) and the group G can be decomposed into left and right cosets as follows[1]

$$G = U \cup g_2 \circ U \cup g_3 \circ U \cup \ldots \cup g_r \circ U = \bigcup_{v=1}^{v=r} g_v \circ U \qquad (33)$$

$$G = U \cup U \circ g_2' \cup U \circ g_3' \cup \ldots \cup U \circ g_r' = \bigcup_{\rho=1}^{\rho=r} U \circ g_\rho' \qquad (33')$$

g_1 and g_1' *stand for the identity element e; for $v \geqslant 2$ and $\rho \geqslant 2$, $g_v \in G$, $g_\rho' \in G$, $g_v \notin U$, $g_\rho' \notin U$.*

The complexes $g_v \circ U$ and $U \circ g_\rho'$ in these decompositions have the following properties:

1) *The intersection of any two complexes of a decomposition is empty:*

$$g_v \circ U \cap g_\mu \circ U = U \circ g_\rho' \cap U \circ g_\sigma' = \varnothing, \qquad v \neq \mu, \qquad \rho \neq \sigma \qquad (34)$$

2) *If g_v^* is any element of $g_v \circ U$ and g_ρ^* any element of $U \circ g_\rho'$, then for these complexes*

$$g_v \circ U = g_v^* \circ U, \qquad U \circ g_\rho' = U \circ g_\rho^* \qquad (35)$$

The last statement can also be worded as follows. In the representations (33), (33') the group elements g_v, g_ρ' can be replaced

---

[1] $\bigcup\limits_{v=1}^{v=n} M_v$ stands for $M_1 \cup M_2 \cup \ldots \cup M_n$.

by *any arbitrary 'representatives'* of the complexes $g_v \circ U$, $U \circ g'_\rho$ respectively.

To prove this theorem we take an arbitrary element g_2 which belongs to G but not to U,[1] and form the complex $g_2 \circ U$.

The elements of this complex do *not* belong to U; for if $g' \in U$, then $g_2 \circ g' = g'' \in U$, and because of the group property we should then also have $g_2 = g'' \circ (g')^{-1} \in U$, contrary to hypothesis.

The complex $g_2 \circ U$ thus contains m elements[2] (the same number as U itself), which are all different from the m elements of U. It follows from this that this complex does *not form a group*; it does not contain the identity element which belongs to U itself. It may happen that by $U \cup g_2 \circ U$ the whole group G is exhausted. We then have only two terms in the representation (33). If this is not the case, then there exists an element g_3 which, although it belongs to G, does not belong to $U \cup g_2 \circ U$.

The complex $g_3 \circ U$ then again contains m elements, which are different from all the elements of $U \cup g_2 \circ U$. For if $g_2 \circ g' = g_3 \circ g''$, where $g' \in U$, $g'' \in U$, then also

$$g_3 = g_2 \circ (g' \circ (g'')^{-1}) = g_2 \circ g^*$$

where $g^* \in U$. g_3 would then be an element of $g_2 \circ U$, contrary to hypothesis.

This process can be continued until, after a finite number of steps, all the elements of G are exhausted. But we have then obtained a representation of the form (33). Since the set on the right hand side of (33) contains $r \, . \, m$ different elements, we must have $r \, . \, m = n$.

The decomposition (33') into right cosets is proved similarly. We still have to prove the statement (35).

If $\gamma_1 = g_\rho \circ g'$ and $\gamma_2 = g_\rho \circ g''$ $(g' \in U,\ g'' \in U)$ are arbitrary different elements of the complex $g_\rho \circ U$, then

$$g_\rho = \gamma_1 \circ (g')^{-1}, \qquad \gamma_2 = \gamma_1 \circ ((g')^{-1}\lambda \circ g'') = \gamma_1 \circ g^*, \qquad g^* \in U$$

Every element of $g_\rho \circ U$ (*e.g.*, γ_2) is therefore also an element of $\gamma_1 \circ U$. Conversely, all elements of

$$\gamma_1 \circ U = g_\rho \circ (g' \circ U) = g_\rho \circ U$$

are clearly also elements of $g_\rho \circ U$. Hence $g_\rho \circ U = \gamma_1 \circ U$, where γ_1 is an arbitrary 'representative' of the coset $g_\rho \circ U$.

---

[1] If $G = U$, then the representation (33) with only one term is already given.
[2] It is easy to show that they are all different.

Two elements of the same coset are called (*left* or *right*) *equivalent with respect to the subgroup U of G*.

$$g_\rho \overset{(l)}{\sim} g_\sigma \Leftrightarrow g_\rho \circ U = g_\sigma \circ U$$

$$g_\rho \overset{(r)}{\sim} g_\sigma \Leftrightarrow U \circ g_\rho = U \circ g_\sigma \tag{36}$$

The definition (36) can also be put in the form

$$g_\rho \overset{(l)}{\sim} g_\sigma \Leftrightarrow g_\rho = g_\sigma \circ g, \qquad g \in U$$

$$g_\rho \overset{(r)}{\sim} g_\sigma \Leftrightarrow g_\rho = g \circ g_\sigma, \qquad g \in U \tag{37}$$

This equivalence relation obviously has the general properties of an equivalence relation which we have noted already for the equivalence of number pairs (see III 57, III 58, and III 59), viz.

$$g_\rho \sim g_\sigma \Leftrightarrow g_\sigma \sim g_\rho$$

$$g_\rho \sim g_\rho$$

$$[(g_\rho \sim g_\sigma) \wedge (g_\sigma \sim g_\tau)] \Rightarrow (g_\rho \sim g_\tau)$$

For groups with a countable number of elements one obtains as a generalization of (33) and (33′) the representation

$$G = U \cup g_2 \circ U \cup g_3 \circ U \cup \ldots = \bigcup_{v=1}^{\infty} g_v \circ U \tag{38}$$

for the decomposition into left cosets, and

$$G = U \cup U \circ g_2' \cup U \circ g_3' \cup \ldots = \bigcup_{v=1}^{\infty} U \circ g_v' \tag{38′}$$

for the decomposition into right cosets.

Let us consider some examples.

(I). The group G_7 of rational numbers (excluding zero) has as subgroups

P: the group of *positive* rational numbers,

U: the group of rational numbers that can be expressed as quotients of *odd* numbers.

These subgroups give rise to the following decompositions of the group G_7

$$G_7 = P \cup (-1) \cdot P = P \cup P \cdot (-1) \tag{39}$$

and

$$G_7 = U \cup 2.U \cup 2^2.U \cup 2^3.U \cup \ldots$$
$$\cup 2^{-1}.U \cup 2^{-2}.U \cup 2^{-3}.U \cup \ldots$$
$$G_7 = U \cup U.2 \cup U.2^2 \cup U.2^3 \cup \ldots \tag{40}$$
$$\cup U.2^{-1} \cup U.2^{-2} \cup U.2^{-3} \cup \ldots$$

These decompositions yield other variations; for example

$$2U = 10U = -14U = U(-14)$$
$$(-1)P = (-3)P = P(-5)$$

(II). The group Z of integers under addition has the subgroup

$$Z_3 = \{0, \pm 3, \pm 6, \pm 9, \ldots\}$$

This yields the decomposition

$$Z = Z_3 \cup (Z_3 + 1) \cup (Z_3 + 2) \tag{41}$$

The set $\{0, 1, 2\}$, and also the triple $\{-15, 31, 5\}$, forms a representative system for the complexes that occur in (41).

(III). The group G_1 defined in IV 1 has already been decomposed into cosets of the subgroups $G_1^{(1)}$ and $G_1^{(3)}$. By (29) and (31) we have

$$s_2 \circ G_1^{(3)} = G_1^{(3)} \circ s_2, \qquad s_3 \circ G_1^{(3)} = G_1^{(3)} \circ s_3$$

For the subgroups $G_1^{(1)}$ and $G_1^{(2)}$ the corresponding equations do not hold. A subgroup U of a group G is called a *normal subgroup* if, for all elements $g \in G$

$$g \circ U = U \circ g$$

$G_1^{(3)}$ is a normal subgroup of G_1, but $G_1^{(1)}$ and $G_1^{(2)}$ are not.

(IV). Let G be a finite group of order m. Every element $g \in G$ is then of finite order. This means (see p. 81) that there exists a smallest natural number r for which $g^r = e$. The elements

$$e, g, g^2, g^3, \ldots, g^{r-1}$$

then form a subgroup of G. Hence by the decomposition theorem r is a divisor of m. Thus we have:

In every finite group G the order of each element $g \in G$ is a divisor of the order of the group.

It follows from this that:

For every group of order m, for all elements $g \in G$,

$$g^m = e \tag{42}$$

This theorem is known as *Fermat's theorem of group theory*, for reasons which will be elaborated later (see V 4).

6. Problems

1. The complex numbers $r + is$ (r and s rational) with the exception of zero form an abelian group under multiplication.
2. The numbers $r + s \cdot \sqrt{2}$ (r and s rational) with the exception of the number zero form an abelian group under multiplication.
3. The vertices of an equilateral triangle are denoted by $1, 2, 3$. Investigate the permutation groups corresponding to those rotations and reflections that bring the triangle into coincidence with itself.
4. The vertices of a square are denoted by $1, 2, 3, 4$ (in a mathematically positive sense). Investigate the permutation groups corresponding to the rotations and reflections that bring the square into coincidence with itself.
5. Examine the corresponding groups for the cube and, in particular, determine its order.
6. A corresponding symmetry group can also be assigned to the octahedron. Show that this group is isomorphic to the group for the cube.
7. The complex numbers $x + iy$ (x and y integers) form a group G_{13} with respect to addition. Decompose this group according to (33) with respect to the subgroup Z of the (real) integers.
8. Let s be the cycle $s = (1\ 2\ 3\ 4\ 5\ 6\ 7)$ and G_{14} the set of permutations

$$G_{14} = \{e = s^0, s, s^2, s^3, s^4, s^5, s^6\}$$

Determine all the subgroups of G_{14}.

CHAPTER FIVE

Rings and Fields

1. Algebraic structures

Several times already we have defined *relations* between the elements of a given set M: the $<$-relationship between integers and the various equivalence relations (p. 66). It is useful to give a general definition for the concept of the relation.

A binary relation in a set M is a set of pairs (a, b) with $a \in M$, $b \in M$.[1]

It may seem strange that we are not concerned here with the particular signs with which the elements a and b are connected (for example $<$ or $\sim$). In fact the notation does not matter (as we saw from the definition of equivalence). What is important is that the relation 'holds' for certain pairs (a, b) and not for others. Another example: in number theory one writes $a|b$ for 'a is a divisor of b'. The set of pairs in this case is the set (a, b) for all the natural numbers a and b for which $a|b$. $(3, 9)$ belongs to the set; $(7, 5)$ and $(8, 2)$ do not.

One must distinguish between relations and *operations*. *A binary operation is a rule which associates with two elements (a and b say) of a set M a third element $v(a, b) = c \in M$.*

For example in Chapter IV we dealt with the binary operation denoted by $\circ$ on elements g and h of a group G. Thus in that case $v(g, h) = g \circ h$. But for the symbol $\circ$ we could also have $+$ or . or yet another sign. We called a set G a group if the binary operation satisfied certain rules which were laid down as group postulates.

A set M with one or more binary operations defined on it (together with corresponding rules for calculation) is called an *algebraic structure*.

A group, for example, is an algebraic structure with *one* binary operation, which satisfies the group postulates G_1 to G_4. But we have met sets on which *more than one* binary operation is

---

[1] Cf. the general definition in the *Begriffsworterbuch* BI 99/a.

defined. For integers and rational numbers, for example, we have introduced binary operations by means of the symbols . and +. Such sets suggest the definition of an algebraic structure with *two* binary operations.

A set R is called a ring if for any two elements $a \in R$ and $b \in R$, a first binary operation $a+b$ and a second binary operation $a \cdot b$ are defined, having the following properties:

R_1: $a+b = b+a$ *(commutative law of addition)*,
R_2: $a+(b+c) = (a+b)+c$ *(associative law of addition)*,
R_3: *For any two elements $a \in R$ and $b \in R$ there exists an element $x \in R$ which satisfies the equation $a+x = b$ (existence of additive inverse)*;
R_4: $a \cdot (b \cdot c) = (a \cdot b) \cdot c$ *(associative law of multiplication)*,
R_5: $a \cdot (b+c) = a \cdot b + a \cdot c, (b+c) \cdot a = b \cdot a + c \cdot a$ *(distributive laws)*.

Here again, the two operations + and . need not have the meaning which is customary for calculations with numbers. We call R a *ring* if, and only if, these five properties of the binary operations are fulfilled.

Note that for a ring the commutative law must hold for addition by R_1, but the second binary operation ('multiplication') need not obey the commutative law. For this reason we had to state two distributive laws under R_5. If for multiplication $a \cdot b = b \cdot a$, then the ring is called *commutative*.

A commutative ring in which division is possible by any element different from the *zero element*[1] is called a *field*. In other words: a commutative ring R is called a field, if for any two elements a and b of R $(a \neq o)$ there exists a well-defined element x for which $a \cdot x = b$.

2. Properties of rings

We now give a few examples of rings. In doing so we shall, in general, omit the sign . for multiplication and thus write ab for $a \cdot b$.

(I). *The set Z of integers forms a ring; and*

(II). *the set Q of rational numbers also has this property.* Both rings are commutative.

(III). The set K_g of complex numbers $x+iy$, where x and y are integers, forms a commutative ring.

---

[1] The existence of at least one zero element o follows at once from R_3 for $a = b$. There is, in fact, *exactly one* zero element (see V 2).

(IV). The set G of even numbers $\{\ldots -6, -4, -2, 0, 2, 4, 6, \ldots\}$ also forms a commutative ring with respect to ordinary addition and multiplication as operations.

(V). It is now time that we gave an example of a ring that is *not commutative*. For this purpose we consider the set T of square matrices

$$\alpha = \begin{pmatrix} a_{11} & a_{12} \\ a_{21} & a_{22} \end{pmatrix}$$

with rational elements a_{ik}. Addition in T is defined by

$$\alpha + \beta = \begin{pmatrix} a_{11} & a_{12} \\ a_{21} & a_{22} \end{pmatrix} + \begin{pmatrix} b_{11} & b_{12} \\ b_{21} & b_{22} \end{pmatrix} = \begin{pmatrix} a_{11}+b_{11} & a_{12}+b_{12} \\ a_{21}+b_{21} & a_{22}+b_{22} \end{pmatrix} \quad (1)$$

Multiplication of these matrices has already been defined in IV 3. Clearly the set T satisfies all the postulates of the ring definition. However, the ring T is not commutative; for example

$$\begin{pmatrix} 1 & 2 \\ 0 & 1 \end{pmatrix} \cdot \begin{pmatrix} 0 & -1 \\ 1 & 0 \end{pmatrix} = \begin{pmatrix} 2 & -1 \\ 1 & 0 \end{pmatrix} \neq \begin{pmatrix} 0 & -1 \\ 1 & 2 \end{pmatrix} = \begin{pmatrix} 0 & -1 \\ 1 & 0 \end{pmatrix} \cdot \begin{pmatrix} 1 & 2 \\ 0 & 1 \end{pmatrix}$$

(VI). The rings considered so far all have infinitely many elements. But this is by no means necessary. We now give an example of a ring with only two elements, the zero and unit elements, which we shall denote by $\circ$ and $|$.

For these two symbols we now define an addition and a multiplication by the following tables:

Addition		
	$\circ$	$|$
$\circ$	$\circ$	$|$
$|$	$|$	$\circ$

Multiplication		
	$\circ$	$|$
$\circ$	$\circ$	$\circ$
$|$	$\circ$	$|$

(2)

Thus, for example,

$$\circ + | = |, \qquad \circ \cdot \circ = \circ, \qquad | + | = \circ \quad (3)$$

One can easily see that the algebraic structure so defined is a commutative ring.

The addition and multiplication defined by (2) have a certain similarity with 'ordinary' addition and multiplication of the numbers 0 and 1 but must not, however, be identified with these as the third equation of (3) shows.

We are familiar, from ordinary calculations with numbers, with the properties R_1 to R_5 of rings. However, it is useful to note that not *all* the laws that are valid for ordinary calculations with numbers can be deduced from R_1 to R_5. This is already shown by the example (VI). But the ring defined in (V) also obeys laws which the rational numbers do not.

For the set Q of rational numbers the following law holds: *if a product is equal to zero, then at least one of the factors must be equal to zero.* This rule does not apply to the ring defined in (V). The zero element $o = \alpha - \alpha$ is in this case given by the matrix

$$o = \begin{pmatrix} 0 & 0 \\ 0 & 0 \end{pmatrix} \tag{4}$$

But we have

$$\gamma \cdot \delta = \begin{pmatrix} 1 & 0 \\ 0 & 0 \end{pmatrix} \cdot \begin{pmatrix} 0 & 0 \\ 0 & 1 \end{pmatrix} = o = \begin{pmatrix} 0 & 0 \\ 0 & 0 \end{pmatrix}$$

Elements γ and δ of a ring, which are different from zero, but for which the product $\gamma \cdot \delta = o$, are called (left and right) zero divisors of the ring.

From the general properties R_1 to R_5 of rings certain propositions can be derived which hold for all rings. To obtain such theorems we first note that every ring, by R_1 to R_3, forms *an abelian group with respect to addition.* Hence all propositions which are valid for such groups (see IV 4) also apply to rings. Therefore, among others, we have the following theorem:

In every ring there exists exactly one zero element.

For in every group there exists one, and only one, identity element. But the identity element *with respect to addition* is the zero element. It is characterized by the equations

$$a + o = o + a = a$$

From the existence of the zero element and by R_3 it follows that: *to every element x of a ring there exists exactly one element $-x$ with the property* $x + (-x) = o$.

From the distributive laws it follows that, for the zero element

$$a \cdot o = o \cdot a = o$$

for all elements a of the ring. Finally we note that, by $\mathbf{R}_4$, we have for *powers* the rules

$$a^m . a^n = a^{m+n} = a^n . a^m$$

In addition, in commutative rings

$$(a . b)^m = a^m . b^m$$

3. Congruences

In order to deal with a number of important examples of finite rings and fields it will be useful to consider first congruence relations between integers.

We have defined an *equivalence relation* by the conditions (75) (p. 66). It is immaterial what symbol ($\sim$, $=$, $\approx$) is used for the binary operation. If a set, in which an addition and a multiplication is defined, apart from (75) (p. 66) also satisfies

$$[(a \sim a_1) \wedge (b \sim b_1)] \Rightarrow [(a+b) \sim (a_1+b_1)] \tag{5}$$

and

$$[(a \sim a_1) \wedge (b \sim b_1)] \Rightarrow (a . b \sim a_1 . b_1) \tag{6}$$

then the binary operation is called a *congruence*.

In Chapter IV we regarded the set Z of integers as a group. In (IV 41) this set was decomposed into cosets

$$Z = Z_3 \cup (Z_3+1) \cup (Z_3+2)$$

where Z_3 was the subgroup

$$Z_3 = \{\ldots -6, -3, 0, 3, 6, \ldots\}$$

of Z. The cosets Z_3+1 and Z_3+2 are the sets

$$Z_3+1 = \{\ldots, -5, -2, +1, +4, +7, \ldots\}$$

$$Z_3+2 = \{\ldots, -4, -1, +2, +5, +8, \ldots\}$$

We can also call these sets 'residue classes modulo 3'. The numbers belonging to the sets Z_3, Z_3+1, Z_3+2 are such that division by 3 gives the remainders 0, 1, 2 respectively.

In Chapter IV we denoted elements belonging to a coset of a group as 'equivalent'. It can be shown that for *residue classes* this equivalence relation has the character of a *congruence*.

Let us consider the residue classes $r_\mu(m)$ which belong to an arbitrary natural number m. These are the m sets of numbers

$$r_\mu(m) = \{\ldots -3m+\mu, -2m+\mu, -m+\mu, \mu, m+\mu, 2m+\mu, 3m+\mu, \ldots\}$$

$$\mu = 0, 1, 2, 3, \ldots, m-1$$

The numbers of the residue class $r_\mu(m)$ (or r_μ modulo m) are such that division by m gives the remainder μ.

The difference of any two numbers of the same residue class is accordingly always divisible by m. This suggests the following definition:

A number a is called *congruent to b* (mod m) if the difference $b-a$ is divisible by m. We write

$$a \equiv b \pmod{m} \tag{7}$$

According to this definition two integers are congruent (mod m) if, and only if, they belong to the same residue class $r_\mu(m)$.

Clearly the binary operation defined by (7) is an equivalence relation. In order to justify the notation 'congruent' we still have to verify the statements corresponding to (5) and (6). Thus, let

$$a \equiv a_1 \pmod{m}, \qquad b \equiv b_1 \pmod{m} \tag{8}$$

This means that $a-a_1$ and $b-b_1$ are both divisible by m. But then $(a-a_1)+(b-b_1) = (a+b)-(a_1+b_1)$ is also a multiple of m, and we have

$$a+b \equiv a_1+b_1 \pmod{m} \tag{9}$$

It also follows from (8) that

$$a.b \equiv a_1.b \pmod{m}, \qquad a_1.b \equiv a_1.b_1 \pmod{m}$$

By the third law of (75) (p. 66) (which also applies to our congruence) we then have as a consequence of (8)

$$a.b \equiv a_1.b_1 \pmod{m} \tag{10}$$

According to the definition of congruence, those, and only those, numbers are congruent that belong to the same residue class. Hence the propositions (9) and (10), which are consequences of (8), can also be formulated as follows:

For all numbers a_μ of the residue class r_μ (mod m) and all numbers b_v of the residue class r_v (mod m) the sums $a_\mu+b_v$ lie in the same residue class $r_{S(\mu,v)}$ and the products $a_\mu.b_v$ lie in the same residue class $r_{P(\mu,v)}$.

Let us consider an example.

The numbers $7, -3, 22, 12$ belong to the residue class r_2 (mod 5) and the numbers $-1, 9, 24, 99$ belong to the residue class r_4 (mod 5). The sums

$$7+(-1),\ 7+9,\ 12+(-1),\ 22+24,\ \ldots$$

of any number from r_2 and any number from r_4 then all belong to r_1. For we have, for example,

$$7-1 = 6 \equiv 1 \ (\text{mod } 5),\ 7+9 = 16 \equiv 1 \ (\text{mod } 5)$$

Similarly for the products we have

$$7\,.\,9 = 63 \equiv 3 \ (\text{mod } 5),\qquad 12\,.\,9 = 108 \equiv 3 \ (\text{mod } 5),\quad \text{etc.}$$

Thus in this case

$$r_{S(2,4)} = r_1, \qquad r_{P(2,4)} = r_3$$

This result suggests a definition of addition and multiplication of the residue classes themselves. We define:

The sum $r_\mu + r_\nu$ of two residue classes (mod m) *is the residue class* $r_{S(\mu,\nu)}$ (mod m), *and the product $r_\mu\,.\,r_\nu$ is the residue class $r_{P(\mu,\nu)}$* (mod m); i.e.

$$r_\mu + r_\nu = r_{S(\mu,\nu)}, \qquad r_\mu \,.\, r_\nu = r_{P(\mu,\nu)} \tag{11}$$

For the residue classes modulo 5 we obtain for the indices $S(\mu, \nu)$ and $P(\mu, \nu)$ of the sum and product the following tables:

$S(\mu, \nu)$ (mod 5)	0	1	2	3	4
0	0	1	2	3	4
1	1	2	3	4	0
2	2	3	4	0	1
3	3	4	0	1	2
4	4	0	1	2	3

$P(\mu, \nu)$ (mod 5)	0	1	2	3	4
0	0	0	0	0	0
1	0	1	2	3	4
2	0	2	4	1	3
3	0	3	1	4	2
4	0	4	3	2	1

The set R_m of the residue classes modulo m obviously forms a commutative ring. It is easy to show that the ring postulates $\boldsymbol{R}_1$ to

R_5 are satisfied. This ring consists of the m elements

$$R_m = \{r_0, r_1, r_2, \ldots, r_{m-1}\}$$

where r_0 has the character of the zero element and r_1 is the unit element with respect to multiplication. For we have for all[1] μ, $(0 \leqslant \mu \leqslant m-1)$, $r_1 \cdot r_\mu = r_\mu \cdot r_1 = r_\mu$.

In the case of the residue classes modulo 5 the set

$$R_5^* = \{r_1, r_2, r_3, r_4\} \ (\text{mod } 5)$$

forms an abelian group with respect to multiplication. On the other hand, the corresponding set for the residue classes modulo 6

$$R_6^* = \{r_1, r_2, r_3, r_4, r_5\} \ (\text{mod } 6)$$

does *not* possess this property. This can be seen by inspection of the product table:

$P(\mu, \nu)$ (mod 6)

	1	2	3	4	5
1	1	2	3	4	5
2	2	4	0	2	4
3	3	0	3	0	3
4	4	2	0	4	2
5	5	4	3	2	1

This table also shows us that there exist zero divisors in the ring of residue classes modulo 6. For example, $r_2 \cdot r_3 = r_0$; *i.e.*, a product of two residue classes, both different from r_0, is the zero element r_0.

Evidently such zero divisors can be found in all residue class rings whose moduli are *not prime numbers*. For these numbers also the set

$$R_m^* = \{r_1, r_2, \ldots, r_{m-1}\} \ (\text{mod } m)$$

does not have the group properties with respect to multiplication. In the ring of residue classes modulo 6 there exists *no unique*

---

[1] Note that every ring has a zero element, but not necessarily a unit element. See Problem V, 4.

multiplicative inverse. For example

$$r_4 \cdot r_2 = r_4 \cdot r_5 = r_2$$

To answer the question as to the conditions under which a ring of residue classes is at the same time a field, which will be considered later, we have to examine the conditions under which a congruence

$$ax \equiv b \pmod{m} \tag{12}$$

has a unique solution x.[1]

We now prove that:

If the natural numbers a and m are relatively prime,[2] then the congruence (12) *has exactly one solution.*

To prove this theorem we note that the numbers

$$a, a \cdot 2, a \cdot 3, \ldots, a \cdot m \tag{13}$$

are pairwise incongruent modulo m.[3] For if $a\mu \equiv a\nu$ ($\mu \neq \nu$, $1 \leqslant \mu \leqslant m$, $1 \leqslant \nu \leqslant m$), then $a(\mu - \nu)$ would be divisible by m. But this is impossible since $0 < |\mu - \nu| < m$.

The numbers (13) therefore form a 'complete set of residues'. This means that *each of the numbers* (13) *is congruent to exactly one of the numbers*

$$0, 1, 2, 3, \ldots, m-1 \tag{14}$$

Now if b is one of these numbers (14) then there exists accordingly exactly one number ax (a number of (13)) which is congruent to it.

4. Fields

By the definition given in V 1 a commutative ring is called a *field* if the equation $ax = b$ has a unique solution when $a \neq o$.

We shall begin with a few examples of rings which do *not* possess the field property.

(I). The ring of integers is not a field, for in general division is not possible: e.g., $2x = 5$ has no integer solution x.

---

[1] Solutions which are congruent modulo m are regarded as identical. By the laws governing congruences we can limit a and b to numbers between 0 and $m-1$ inclusive.

[2] The greatest common divisor (g.c.d.) of a and m is thus 1; we write $(a, m) = 1$.

[3] a is called incongruent to b (mod m) if the statement $a \equiv b$ (mod m) is false.

(II). The set T of square matrices (see example (V) of V 2) forms a *non-commutative* ring. Hence it is certainly not a field.

(III). The ring of residue classes modulo 6 does not form a field. We have already seen from the product table on p. 101 that the division problem is not uniquely soluble.

From our remarks about zero divisors in residue classes we may add that all those residue classes whose moduli are not prime numbers do not form fields.

We shall now give a few examples of rings which are also fields.

(IV). The set Q of rational numbers forms a field. The field properties follow at once from the theorems about rational numbers which were derived in Chapter 3.

(V). The set K_r of complex numbers $r + is$ (with rational r and s) forms a field.

(VI). The set of residue classes $\{r_0, r_1, \ldots, r_{p-1}\}$ modulo a prime number p forms a field. This follows at once from the last theorem of V 3 about the congruence $ax = b \pmod{m}$. If m is a prime number, then $(a, m) = 1$ for all numbers a with $0 < a < m$.

The question arises as to whether one can construct a field from the set of residue classes modulo an arbitrary number, by disregarding certain residue classes. For the zero divisors in the rings of residue classes are provided by those classes whose indices have a common factor with m. For example, in the ring of residue classes modulo 6, we have the zero divisors r_2 and r_3 for which $r_2 . r_3 = r_0$.

One can see at once, however, that the ring character of the set will be destroyed even if only *one* element is disregarded; for in a ring, addition and multiplication must be possible without exception. In the ring of residue classes modulo 6, for example, r_2 is a zero divisor. Since $r_1 + r_1 = r_2$, the zero divisor cannot be disregarded.

However it is possible, by disregarding certain elements of a ring of residue classes, to obtain a set which at least forms a *group with respect to multiplication*.

Among the numbers $1, 2, 3, \ldots, m-1$ there will be a certain number[1] $\phi(m)$ of numbers which are relatively prime to m. For a prime number p, clearly

$$\phi(p) = p - 1 \tag{15}$$

For prime powers we have

$$\phi(p^a) = p^a - p^{a-1} \tag{15'}$$

---

[1] This function $\phi(m)$ is called the Euler function.

For arbitrary numbers m with prime factorization $m = p_1 p_2 \cdots p_r$ the Euler function can be expressed in the form[1]

$$\phi(m) = m \prod_{\rho=1}^{r} \left(1 - \frac{1}{p_\rho}\right) \tag{16}$$

Now let

$$\tilde{R}_m = \{r_{\rho_1}, r_{\rho_2}, \dots, r_{\rho_{\phi(m)}}\}$$

be the set of residue classes modulo m for which the index is relatively prime to m, i.e., $(\rho_v, m) = 1$. *This set $\tilde{R}_m$ forms a group with respect to the multiplication defined for the residue classes.*

For it contains the identity element r_1. The product of two such residue classes is again a residue class of $\tilde{R}_m$; since the product of two numbers which are relatively prime to m is again relatively prime to m. The existence of the inverse element follows from the fact that the linear congruence

$$\rho_v \cdot x \equiv 1 \pmod{m}$$

has a unique solution, by the theorem (see V 3) on linear congruences. If x and m had a common divisor, then $\rho_v \cdot x$ and m would also have a common divisor, and this number could not then be congruent to 1 (mod m).

Since, of course, the associative law is also valid for the multiplication, $\tilde{R}_m$ is indeed a group.

We now apply to this group *Fermat's theorem of group theory* (see IV, 42). In this case it takes the form

$$r_{\rho_v}^{\phi(m)} = r_1 \quad (v = 1, 2, 3, \dots, \phi(m)) \tag{17}$$

But (17) can also be written in the form of a proposition about numbers which belong to the various residue classes.

For all natural numbers a that are relatively prime to m,

$$a^{\phi(m)} \equiv 1 \pmod{m} \tag{18}$$

For $m = 12$ we have[2] $\phi(12) = 4$, and by (18) we find, for example,

$$5^4 = 625 \equiv 1 \pmod{12}, \qquad 7^4 = 2401 \equiv 1 \pmod{12}$$

[1] See, for example, B. Haupt, p. 116.
[2] For the number 12 there are four relatively prime numbers $n < 12$: $n = 1, 5, 7, 11$.

In particular, for the prime number p we have by (17)

$$a^{p-1} \equiv 1 \pmod{p} \tag{19}$$

This is the so-called 'little Fermat theorem' which was formulated in Exercise 4 of Chapter III in a somewhat different form.

From this example the significance of the 'formalistic' method of modern mathematics will become clear. The little Fermat theorem in the form (19) has been known for a long time, and also its generalization (18). Group theory enables us to take a significant step further. It is possible to derive for finite groups the theorem (IV, 42) which can now be interpreted as a far-reaching generalization of a well known number theoretical theorem.

We may expect that the examination of basic mathematical structures will always allow us to make similar extensions of known concepts.

5. Formal systems

Up to now we have been concerned, as a rule, with sets whose elements consisted of numbers or sets of numbers (matrices, residue classes). There is, however, no reason to confine concepts such as ring, group, and field to number sets only.

In Example (VI) of V 2 we have already become acquainted with a ring whose elements were the two symbols $\circ$ and $|$. These symbols bear a certain similarity to the numbers 0 and 1, but their rule of addition (cf. the table on p. 96) does not agree with that for the numbers 0 and 1. Incidentally it is easily shown that this ring also possesses the properties of a field.

We shall now construct fields which contain 3, 4 elements respectively. Since every field must contain a zero and a unit element, it is convenient to use again for these elements the symbols $\circ$ and $|$. As a third symbol we now add the vertical arrow $\uparrow$.

It is not difficult to build a field with these three symbols. One has only to bear in mind that the ring of residue classes modulo 3 has exactly the three elements $r_0, r_1,$ and r_2. If we now write $\circ$ for r_0, $|$ for r_1, and finally $\uparrow$ for r_2, then we can take over the rules of the binary operations of this residue class (which, moreover, is a field) for the set of symbols $\circ$, $|$, and $\uparrow$.

By carrying over to arbitrary algebraic structures the notation which we introduced for groups (see IV 4) we can call

$$M_3 = \{\circ, |, \uparrow\}$$

a field which is isomorphic[1] to the field of residue classes modulo 3.

A field with four elements cannot be constructed on the basis of residue classes. Since 4 is not a prime number, the ring of residue classes modulo 4 is not a field (see V 4).

Here we proceed as follows. For the set

$$M_4 = \{°, |, ↑, ↓\}$$

we define addition and multiplication by the following tables:

Addition						Multiplication		
°	|	↑	↓			|	↑	↓
°	°	|	↑	↓		|	|	↑	↓
|	|	°	↓	↑		↑	↑	↓	|
↑	↑	↓	°	|		↓	↓	|	↑
↓	↓	↑	|	°					

FIG. 17.

The multiplication table does not contain the zero element °. The product of any element with ° is, of course, always equal to °. From the tables one can see at once that addition and multiplication are *commutative*. The reader should convince himself that the ring property R_2 is satisfied; *i.e.*, the associative law holds for addition. For example

$$(↓+↑)+| = |+| = ° = ↓+↓ = ↓+(↑+|)$$

The uniqueness of the additive inverse (rule R_3) follows at once from the fact that each row and each column of the table contains

---

[1] In general, an algebraic structure A is *isomorphic* to an algebraic structure A^* if the following conditions are satisfied:

1. Between the elements of A and those of A^* there exists a one-to-one mapping
$$a \leftrightarrow a^* \quad (a \in A, a^* \in A^*)$$

2. In A and A^* the same binary operations are defined and for every such operation $v(a, b)$, $v(a^*, b^*)$ respectively,
$$(v(a, b))^* = v(a^*, b^*)$$

each element of M_4 exactly once. The corresponding result holds for multiplication by factors different from ○. The distributive laws are also satisfied. We have, for example,

$$\uparrow(\uparrow + \downarrow) = \uparrow . | = \uparrow$$
$$\uparrow\uparrow + \uparrow\downarrow = \downarrow + | = \uparrow$$

Hence we have shown that M_4 is a ring with respect to the binary operations defined by the tables and (because of the uniqueness of the multiplicative inverse) it is also a field.

A reader with a somewhat conservative outlook might object to the definition of M_4 and maintain that here mathematics 'degenerates' to a formal game with arbitrary symbols. In fact we are no longer concerned with numbers or geometrical objects for which a relationship with the 'real world' can easily be discerned. Here, and in many other branches of modern mathematics, we deal with 'formal systems', and unsympathetic critics could call that a game.

However, it shows that this kind of game is of great significance. Apart from the insight into the theory of knowledge which has been achieved by the study of such formal systems,[1] there are situations in modern physics which make it necessary to introduce new formal systems as objects of mathematical study. The mathematician does not wait until a specific physical problem requires the investigation of one or another mathematical structure. He has always tackled problems for which technical or physical applications could not be foreseen. The theory of integral equations, for example, was developed at a time when physicists were not yet aware of how important this new branch of mathematics would become to them one day. And so today also we shall not refrain from developing mathematics as the 'science of formal systems' without always asking about the 'usefulness' of the results.

6. Problems

1. Define for the set
$$M_5 = \{○, |, \uparrow, \downarrow, \leftarrow\}$$

an addition and a multiplication according to the pattern of Chapter III, in such a way that M_5 is a field isomorphic to the field of residue classes modulo 5.

[1] See, for example, Meschkowski (2), Chapters X and XI.

2. Show that a natural number

$$n = c_0 + c_1 10 + \ldots + c_r 10^r$$

is divisible by 9 if

$$q = c_0 + c_1 + \ldots + c_r$$

is divisible by 9, and is divisible by 11 if

$$q' = c_0 - c_1 + \ldots + (-1)^r c_r$$

is divisible by 11.

3. A ring is called an *integral domain*[1] if it possesses the following properties:

   a) If $ab = ac$ and $a \neq o$ it follows that $b = c$.
   b) There exists a unit element e such that $ae = a$.

   Show that *if the product of two elements of an integral domain is equal to zero, then at least one of the factors is equal to zero.*

4. Give an example of a) a ring that is not an integral domain; b) an integral domain that is not a field.

5. The 'dual numbers' are defined by $a + b\varepsilon$, where a and b are rational numbers and $\varepsilon^2 = o$. Examine whether the dual numbers form a) a ring, b) an integral domain.

6. Prove that, for any two elements a and b of the field M defined in V 5

$$(a+b)^2 = a^2 + (|+|)ab + b^2$$

7. Replace the addition defined for the set M_4 of V 5 by an addition defined by the following table:

	○			↑	↓
○	○			↑	↓
				↑	↓	○
↑	↑	↓	○		
↓	↓	○			↑

FIG. 18.

Examine whether M_4 forms a ring under this addition and the multiplication defined on p. 106.

[1] By an integral domain one frequently understands a zero divisor-free commutative ring.

CHAPTER SIX

Lattices

1. Graphs

In IV 1 we were concerned with the 'tetrahedral group' G_1. It consists of 12 permutations of degree 4. The sets $G_1^{(1)}$, $G_1^{(2)}$ and $G_1^{(3)}$, defined by (IV, 27), are subgroups of G_1. We now note that the subgroup $G_1^{(3)}$ in turn possesses the three subgroups

$$G_1^{(31)} = \{s_1, s_{10}\}, \qquad G_1^{(32)} = \{s_1, s_{11}\}, \qquad G_1^{(33)} = \{s_1, s_{12}\}$$

The complexes $G_1^{(4)} = \{s_1, s_6, s_7\}$ and $G_1^{(5)} = \{s_1, s_8, s_9\}$ are also subgroups of G_1. If we also include the subgroup $E = \{s_1\}$, which consists of the identity element s_1, then we have all the subgroups of G_1.

One obtains a pictorial representation of the connection between the different subgroups by representing them in the form of a 'graph'. This consists of a scheme of lines connecting the individual elements[1] (which are conveniently indicated by circles). If G_ν is below G_μ and G_ν and G_μ are connected by a line, then G_ν is a sub-group of G_μ. Fig. 19 shows the graph of the group G_1.

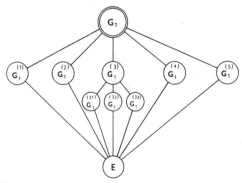

Fig. 19.

[1] See, for example, Meschkowski (3), Chapter VII.

For the group G_3 defined in IV 3 the structure of the corresponding graph is even simpler. Here we have the subgroups

$$U_1 = \{f_1, f_2\}, \qquad U_2 = \{f_1, f_3\},$$
$$U_3 = \{f_1, f_4\}, \qquad U_4 = \{f_1, f_5, f_6\}$$

and obviously also the subgroup $E = \{f_1\}$ which consists of the identity element. The graph of this group is shown in Fig. 20.

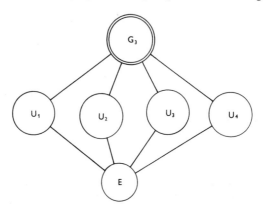

FIG. 20.

The structure of the graph of a group can, of course, be more complicated, but in every case we have at the top of the graph (*i.e.*, in the first line) the given group and at the bottom (*i.e.*, in the last line) the subgroup which consists of the identity element.

One can also use the representation by graphs to show the connection between the factors of a natural number. For example the number 45 has the prime factorization $45 = 3 . 3 . 5$. Hence 45 has two factors which are the product of two prime numbers, viz. $9 = 3 . 3$ and $15 = 3 . 5$. We write these numbers below 45 and connect them with 45 by a line (Fig. 21). 15 has the factors 3 and 5 and 9 the factor 3. We write the numbers 3 and 5 below the numbers 9 and 15 and again connect the numbers in such a way as to indicate the divisibility. Each line connects a number with a factor lying below it. If we add 1 as a factor of the prime numbers 3 and 5 we then obtain the graph of the number 45.

Fig. 22 shows the corresponding graph for the number 60. For powers of prime numbers the graph 'degenerates' into a chain (Fig. 23).

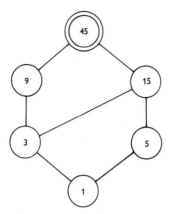

FIG. 21.

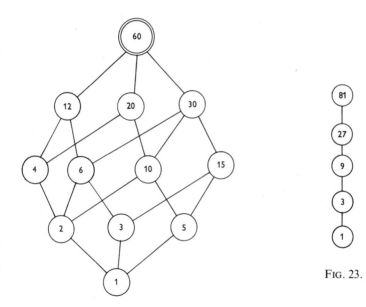

FIG. 22.

FIG. 23.

In the graph of a natural number each number is connected by a line or a train of lines with each of its factors. This enables one to determine easily the common divisors and the common multiples of two numbers in a graph. In particular one can also read off the least common multiple (l.c.m.) and the greatest common divisor (g.c.d.). If we denote the g.c.d. of two natural numbers a and b by $a \sqcap b$

$$\text{g.c.d. } (a, b) = a \sqcap b \tag{1}$$

and similarly the l.c.m. of a and b by $a \sqcup b$

$$\text{l.c.m. } (a, b) = a \sqcup b \tag{2}$$

then, for example, from Fig. 22

$$20 \sqcap 30 = 10, \qquad 20 \sqcup 30 = 60$$

$$30 \sqcap 6 = 6, \qquad 30 \sqcup 6 = 30$$

This symbolism can be carried over to graphs of groups. For this purpose we define for the subgroups U_ν of a group G:

$U_\nu \sqcap U_\mu =$ the greatest subgroup of G which is a subgroup of U_ν and U_μ,

$U_\nu \sqcup U_\mu =$ the smallest subgroup of G which contains U_ν and U_μ as subgroups.

For example, for the group G_1 (Fig. 19)

$$G_1^{(3)} \sqcap G_1^{(2)} = E, \qquad G_1^{(3)} \sqcup G_1^{(2)} = G_1$$

$$G_1^{(31)} \sqcap G_1^{(32)} = E, \qquad G_1^{(31)} \sqcup G_1^{(32)} = G_1^{(3)}$$

Note that $U_\nu \sqcap U_\mu$ must not simply be identified with the intersection $U_\nu \cap U_\mu$, nor $U_\nu \sqcup U_\mu$ with the union $U_\nu \cup U_\mu$. For example, the union $G_1^{(31)} \cup G_1^{(32)} = \{s_1, s_{10}, s_{11}\}$ is not a group.

The symbols $\sqcap$ and $\sqcup$ (for both interpretations given here) satisfy rules which are analagous to the rules (II, 18a) to (II, 18c) and (II, 19a) to (II, 19c)

$$a \sqcap b = b \sqcap a \tag{3a}$$

$$(a \sqcap b) \sqcap c = a \sqcap (b \sqcap c) \tag{3b}$$

$$a \sqcap (a \sqcup b) = a \tag{3c}$$

$$a \sqcup b = b \sqcup a \tag{4a}$$

$$(a \sqcup b) \sqcup c = a \sqcup (b \sqcup c) \tag{4b}$$

$$a \sqcup (a \sqcap b) = a \tag{4c}$$

The justification of these rules (for application to both numbers and groups) will be left to the reader.

2. Definition of a lattice

A set V (with elements a, b, c, . . .) is called a lattice if binary operations ⊓ and ⊔ are defined in V, which satisfy the axioms (3a) to (3c) and (4a) to (4c).

It is, of course, not essential to use the symbols ⊓ and ⊔ for the operations. They can, for example, be replaced by ∩ and ∪, provided that these symbols satisfy the 'lattice axioms' (3a) to (4c).

According to the results of VI 1 we can interpret the numbers that occur in the graph of the number 60 (Fig. 22) as elements of a lattice, where the binary operations $a \sqcap b$ and $a \sqcup b$ are defined by (1) and (2). The set of subgroups of a given group G also forms a lattice according to VI 1.

All the examples of lattices given so far contain a finite number of elements. This, however, is not expressly required by the lattice axioms. We shall now look for examples of infinite sets which can be interpreted as lattices.

Let M be an arbitrary infinite set, and let $P(M)$ be the corresponding power set (see II 3). We replace the symbols ⊓ and ⊔ by the symbols ∩ and ∪ for intersection and union respectively. Since for these binary operations the rules (II, 18a) to (II, 19c) are valid, the set[1] $\{P(M); \cap, \cup\}$ is a lattice with infinitely many elements.

The set N of natural numbers provides a further example of a lattice with infinitely many elements, if for this set the following binary operations are introduced

$$a \sqcap b = \text{Max}(a, b), \qquad a \sqcup b = \text{Min}(a, b)$$

where $\text{Max}(a, b)$ denotes the larger and $\text{Min}(a, b)$ the smaller of the two numbers a and b. More precisely

$$\text{Max}(a, b) = \begin{cases} a, & \text{if } b \leqslant a, \\ b, & \text{if } a \leqslant b, \end{cases} \qquad \text{Min}(a, b) = \begin{cases} a, & \text{if } a \leqslant b, \\ b, & \text{if } b \leqslant a \end{cases}$$

Before giving further examples of lattices, we shall derive some simple theorems which hold for all lattices.

$$a \sqcup a = a \qquad (5)$$

---

[1] Since a lattice is not defined by the set of its elements alone, but only when the two binary operations are laid down, it is often characterized in the form $(V; \sqcap, \sqcup)$. One can omit the symbols if there is no possibility of ambiguity.

To prove (5) we replace the second a in $a \sqcup a$ according to (3c) as follows

$$a \sqcup a = a \sqcup [a \sqcap (a \sqcup b)]$$

Writing c for $a \sqcup b$, we have

$$a \sqcup a = a \sqcup [a \sqcap c] \qquad (6)$$

Since in our lattice axioms we may replace the letters a, b, and c for the elements by any other letters, we also have by (4c)

$$a \sqcup [a \sqcap c] = a$$

and our proposition (5) follows from (6).

We now show that

$$(a \sqcap b = a \sqcup b) \Rightarrow a = b \qquad (7)$$

Assume that the left hand side of the implication (7) is satisfied. Then, using (4b) and (5), it follows from (4c) that

$$a = a \sqcup (a \sqcap b) = a \sqcup (a \sqcup b) = (a \sqcup a) \sqcup b = a \sqcup b$$

Similarly we can show that $b = a \sqcup b$, and it then follows that $a = b$.

Finally we justify the following implication

$$[(a \sqcup b) = a] \Rightarrow [(a \sqcap b) = b] \qquad (8)$$

To prove this we interchange a and b in (3c), viz.

$$b = b \sqcap (b \sqcup a)$$

It follows from (4a) that

$$b = b \sqcap (a \sqcup b)$$

If now $a \sqcup b = a$, it follows that $b \sqcap a = b$, and by (3a) we have finally

$$a \sqcap b = b$$

Our lattice axioms exhibit a remarkable symmetry. If we interchange the symbols $\sqcap$ and $\sqcup$ we obtain from the axioms (3a) to (3c) the statements (4a) to (4c), and vice versa. We shall therefore call the statements (3a) and (4a), (3b) and (4b), (3c) and (4c) mutually *dual* axioms. If in any lattice theoretical proof we replace each of the axioms which we use by its dual, then we obtain the proof of a new proposition, which is the *dual* of the original one.

Any proposition which is deduced from the lattice axioms only is called a lattice theoretical theorem. For such theorems (by the above considerations) we have the

Principle of duality of lattice theory:
For every lattice theoretical theorem the dual theorem holds.

We shall apply this principle to the theorems which we have just proved. Interchanging the symbols $\sqcap$ and $\sqcup$ we obtain from (5), (7), and (8) the dual theorems

$$a \sqcap a = a \tag{5'}$$

$$[(a \sqcup b) = (a \sqcap b)] \Rightarrow a = b \tag{7'}$$

and

$$[a \sqcap b = a] \Rightarrow [a \sqcup b = b] \tag{8'}$$

The propositions (5′) and (8′) are different from the dual theorems (5) and (8). On the other hand, because of the symmetry of the equality, the propositions (7) and (7′) are equivalent. We say that the proposition (7) is *self-dual*.

So far we have derived only theorems which could be justified directly from the lattice axioms. It is, however, possible to define special lattices by means of particular properties. For these special lattices the principle of duality is then valid only if the characteristic properties are dual.

Consider an example. A lattice is called *distributive* if it satisfies the laws

$$a \sqcap (b \sqcup c) = (a \sqcap b) \sqcup (a \sqcap c) \tag{9}$$

and

$$a \sqcup (b \sqcap c) = (a \sqcup b) \sqcap (a \sqcup c) \tag{10}$$

An example of a distributive lattice is the power set of a given set M. Here the symbols $\sqcap$ and $\sqcup$ are replaced by the set theoretical symbols $\cap$ and $\cup$ for which, by (II 22) and (II 23), the laws (9) and (10) are valid.

On the other hand the lattice of the subgroups belonging to the group G_3 (with the graph shown in Fig. 20) is *not* distributive. For example

$$U_1 \sqcup (U_2 \sqcap U_3) = U_1 \sqcup E = U_1$$

but

$$(U_1 \sqcup U_2) \sqcap (U_1 \sqcup U_3) = G_3 \sqcap G_3 = G_3$$

For every distributive lattice the duality principle holds.

This means that for every theorem derived from the lattice axioms *and* one of the distributive laws (9) or (10), the dual theorem holds. This is a direct consequence of the fact that the two distributive laws (9) and (10) are mutually dual.

3. Partially ordered sets

A glance at Figs. 19–23 shows that lattices exhibit certain order relations. The regularities that can be observed do not, however, correspond to the two axioms O_1 and O_2 for the antireflexive ordering of II 7.

For example, if one were to enumerate the elements of the graph of Fig. 19 from 'bottom' to 'top', then one could certainly state that $G_1^{(31)}$ occurred 'before' $G_1^{(3)}$, but among the subgroups $G_1^{(31)}$, $G_1^{(32)}$, and $G_1^{(33)}$ one could not speak of 'preceding' or 'succeeding'.

Also axiom O_1 cannot be applied here, if U_ν before U_μ ($U_\nu \prec U_\mu$) is interpreted to mean that U_ν is a subgroup of U_μ. For, according to the definition, every element U_ν is a subgroup of U_ν itself; thus we should have $U_\nu \prec U_\nu$.

To describe the ordering in a lattice a new definition is required.

A set M (with elements a, b, c, . . .) is called a partially ordered set if a binary relation **u** *is defined in M,*[1] *which satisfies the following axioms:*

$$a \, \mathbf{u} \, a \tag{11a}$$

$$[(a \, \mathbf{u} \, b) \wedge (b \, \mathbf{u} \, c)] \Rightarrow (a \, \mathbf{u} \, c) \tag{11b}$$

$$[(a \, \mathbf{u} \, b) \wedge (b \, \mathbf{u} \, a)] \Rightarrow b = a \tag{11c}$$

As a first example of a partially ordered set we mention the set Q of rational numbers with the binary relation $\leqslant$ in place of the general symbol **u**. The axioms (11a) to (11c) clearly hold for this relation. However, the symbol $<$ belongs to an antireflexive ordering in the sense of II 7.

The power set $P(M)$ of a given set M is also a partially ordered set. Here the set theoretical symbol $\subset$ provides the binary relation.[2]

---

[1] $a \, \mathbf{u} \, b$ is read '*a* below *b*'.

[2] In the literature one finds the sign $\leqslant$ or the set theoretical symbol $\subset$ in the formulation of the axioms. We prefer (just as for groups and lattices) to use in the axioms of a structure a different sign from that used in special cases.

There is a remarkable difference between the two partially ordered sets just mentioned. For any two rational numbers p and q we always have either $p \leqslant q$ or $q \leqslant p$. If *both* relations hold, then $p = q$. However, for two elements of a power set $P(M)$, there by no means always exists a relation $A \subset B$ or $B \subset A$ (see Figs. 7a, b or 8). The definition of a partially ordered set does not require that for any two elements a and b, at least one of the relations $a \, \mathbf{u} \, b$ or $b \, \mathbf{u} \, a$ must always hold. *If* that is the case, then the partially ordered set is called a *simply ordered set or a chain.*

Definition: a partially ordered set H is called a simply ordered set (or a chain) if for any two elements $a \in H$, $b \in H$ at least one of the relations $a \, \mathbf{u} \, b$ or $b \, \mathbf{u} \, a$ is satisfied.

All the lattices given as examples in VI 1 are also partially ordered sets. For the sets of subgroups the relation $U_{\mu} \, \mathbf{u} \, U_{\nu}$ must be interpreted as meaning that U_{μ} is a subgroup of U_{ν}. For the lattices given by the factors of a number, $a \, \mathbf{u} \, b$ stands for $a|b$ (*i.e.*, a is a factor of b, or a divides b).

Of the above examples the following partially ordered sets are at the same time also simply ordered sets, or chains:

a) the set Q of rational numbers with the relation $\leqslant$,
b) the lattice of the factors of 81, shown in Fig. 23, with the relation given by the symbol $|$ ('divides').

It is useful to introduce the following notation for partially ordered sets. We say that an element b with $b \neq a, b \neq c$ lies *between* a and c if $a \, \mathbf{u} \, b$ and $b \, \mathbf{u} \, c$. a is called the *lower neighbour* of b (and b the *upper neighbour* of a) if $a \, \mathbf{u} \, b$ and $a \neq b$ and *no element of the partially ordered set different from a and b lies between a and b.*

In the partially ordered set of rational numbers there are no neighbours; for between any two rational numbers there always lies another rational number. On the other hand, such neighbours exist for the partially ordered sets defined by the graphs of VI 1. For example, for the partially ordered set given by the lattice of the group G_1 (Fig. 19), $G_1^{(31)}$ is the lower neighbour of $G_1^{(3)}$, $G_1^{(3)}$ the lower neighbour of G_1. $G_1^{(31)}$ is the upper neighbour of E.

An element of a partially ordered set that lies below all the remaining elements is called the *null element* of the set. If there exists an element that lies above all the remaining elements, then we call it the *universal element.*

All the graphs of Figs. 19–23 represent not only lattices but also partially ordered sets with null and universal element. For graphs that belong to a group, the given group is always the universal element and the subgroup E the null element. For the graph of a natural number (Figs. 21–23), the given number is the universal element and the number 1 is the null element.

The set Q of rational numbers is a partially ordered set (and moreover a chain) *without* null or universal element. The set of non-negative rational numbers is a partially ordered set with a null element but without a universal element.

There are also finite partially ordered sets without null or universal elements. The simplest way to see this is from the corresponding graphs of these sets. These graphs are obtained by connecting neighbours by lines in such a way that the lower neighbour is always placed 'below' the upper neighbour. With this proviso it is also possible to use graphs to define partially ordered sets.

Figs. 24 and 25 show graphs of partially ordered sets which do not contain null or universal elements.

The element a of Fig. 24 lies below c, d, e, and f but not below b. Hence it is not a null element. In the same way e and f are not universal elements. Nevertheless, the elements a and b are characterized by the fact that no element different from a and b lies below them. Such elements are said to be *minimal*. Similarly elements are called *maximal* if no element of the partially ordered set lies above them. Thus the graph of Fig. 24 represents a partially ordered set without null and universal elements, in which elements a and b are minimal and elements e and f are maximal.

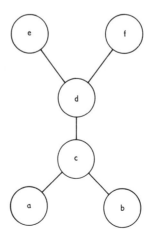

FIG. 24.

The graph shown in Fig. 25 consists of two parts between which no ordering relation exists. Such a situation is permissible for a partially ordered set. In this graph the elements a and b are minimal but neither of the two is a null element.

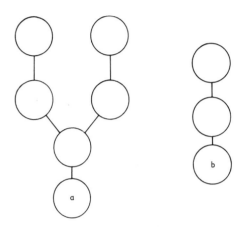

FIG. 25.

Several times already we have interpreted lattices as partially ordered sets. In fact this can always be done.

Every lattice is a partially ordered set in which the relation $a \, \mathbf{u} \, b$ is defined by

$$a \, \mathbf{u} \, b \Leftrightarrow a \sqcap b = a \qquad (12)$$

By (8′) this can also be written as

$$a \, \mathbf{u} \, b \Leftrightarrow a \sqcup b = b \qquad (12')$$

It is not difficult to verify that the axioms (11a), (11b), and (11c) for partially ordered sets are satisfied by the definition (12). For $a \, \mathbf{u} \, a$ implies $a \sqcap a = a$, which is correct, by (5′). By (12) the premise of the implication (11b) can be written

$$a \sqcap b = a, \qquad b \sqcap c = b$$

But we then have

$$a \sqcap c = (a \sqcap b) \sqcap c = a \sqcap (b \sqcap c) = a \sqcap b = a$$

Thus by (12) we also have $a \, \mathbf{u} \, c$.

Finally if a **u** b and b **u** a, then by (12) this means that $a \sqcap b = a$, $b \sqcap a = b$. It follows that $a = b$.

It is possible to ascribe an *order-theoretical* meaning to the relations $a \sqcap b$ and $a \sqcup b$ for any arbitrary lattice. For this purpose we introduce the concepts of *upper bound* and *least upper bound* for partially ordered sets.

Let H' be an arbitrary subset of a partially ordered set H. An element $s \in H$ is called an *upper bound* of H', if a **u** s holds for all elements $a \in H'$.

For example, the number 17 in the partially ordered set of rational numbers is an upper bound for the subset Q' of rational numbers between 1 and 2. For the subset $H' = \{a, b, c\}$ of the partially ordered set represented by the graph of Fig. 24 each of the elements c, d, e, and f is an upper bound. On the other hand the subset H'', consisting of the elements e and f, has no upper bound.

If there exists a smallest[1] upper bound g for a subset A, then it is called the *least upper bound* (or *supremum*) and denoted by

$$g = \sup A$$

Similarly one defines the *lower bounds* and the *greatest lower bound* (or *infimum*)

$$h = \inf A$$

The subset $H' = \{a, b, c\}$ of the partially ordered set represented in Fig. 24 has the upper bound c; it has, however, no lower bound. Note that c **u** c holds, so that c has the character of a bound for H'. But a and b are not lower bounds, since a does not lie below b, nor b below a.

It may well happen that upper bounds exist for a subset of a partially ordered set, but no least upper bound. An example of this is the subset Q'' of the set Q of rational numbers whose square does not exceed 2

$$Q'' = \{x/x \in Q \wedge x^2 \leqslant 2\}$$

The number $1 \cdot 5$ is an upper bound for Q'' but, as is well known,[2] there is no least upper bound for this set, since $\sqrt{2}$ is not rational.

We shall now show that:

In a lattice any two elements a and b of the associated partially ordered set have the element $a \sqcup b$ as least upper bound and the element $a \sqcap b$ as greatest lower bound.

---

[1] The smallest upper bound is characterized by the fact that it lies *below* all the upper bounds.

[2] See, for example, Meschkowski (2), p. 8 et seq.

We prove that

$$a \sqcap b = \inf(a, b) \tag{13}$$

The proof of

$$a \sqcup b = \sup(a, b) \tag{14}$$

is similar and is left to the reader.

To prove (13) we write (4c), using (4a), in the form

$$(a \sqcap b) \sqcup a = a$$

By (12') this means that

$$a \sqcap b \mathbf{u} a$$

Interchanging a and b we obtain the corresponding result

$$a \sqcap b \mathbf{u} b$$

This means that $a \sqcap b$ *is a common lower bound for a and b.* We must now show that it is the *greatest* lower bound. In other words we must prove that $c \mathbf{u} a \sqcap b$ holds for all elements c of the lattice that lie below a and b.

Assume then that for any element c the relations $c \mathbf{u} a$ and $c \mathbf{u} b$ are satisfied. By the definition (12) we then have

$$c \sqcap a = c, \qquad c \sqcap b = c$$

Then, by (5'), (4b), and (4a)

$$c \sqcap (a \sqcap b) = (c \sqcap c) \sqcap (a \sqcap b) = (c \sqcap a) \sqcap (c \sqcap b) = c \sqcap c = c$$

But this means that $c \mathbf{u} a \sqcap b$.

Thus *every lattice can be interpreted as a partially ordered set.* Conversely one can show that:

A partially ordered set H, in which any two elements a and b possess a least upper bound and a greatest lower bound, can be interpreted as a lattice with the definition

$$a \sqcap b = \inf(a, b), \qquad a \sqcup b = \sup(a, b)$$

To prove this theorem one has to show that the binary relations so defined satisfy the lattice axioms.[1]

We shall not enter further into the general theory of lattices.[2]

---

[1] See, for example, Hermes, pp. 12 and 10.
[2] See Hermes and Gericke.

But in order to illustrate the wide scope of applications of these structures we shall consider two particularly important realizations of the lattice axioms.

4. Tautologies

According to II 2, the truth value of a logical formula[1] such as

$$A \Rightarrow (A \Rightarrow B) \tag{15}$$

or

$$\neg A \Rightarrow (A \Rightarrow B) \tag{16}$$

can be determined from Table (II, 10). From this table it can be seen that the implication $A \Rightarrow C$ is false only if A is true and C is false. One recognizes from this that formula (15) represents a *false* proposition if A is true and B false. In all other cases (15) is true.

The proposition (16), on the other hand, is always true, whatever truth values are given to the individual propositions A and B. The quickest way to see this is as follows. If A is true, then the negation $\neg A$ is false, and hence the whole proposition (16) is true, since an implication with a false premise is true according to (II, 10). There still remains the case in which A is false. Then—again by (II, 10)—the implication within the bracket in (16) is true. The complete proposition is then an implication between two true propositions, and is thus certainly true. In all these considerations the truth value of proposition B did not matter.

A logical formula $F(A_1, A_2, A_3, \ldots, A_n)$ which is true for all possible truth values of the propositions A_ν $(\nu = 1, 2, 3, \ldots, n)$ is called a *tautology*. The study of tautologies is one of the most important tasks of propositional calculus.

One could remark that propositions that are true for all possible truth values of the proposition variables must necessarily be empty of content. This is certainly true, and yet the study of tautologies leads to important insight into the theory of knowledge. We shall mention only one fact.[2] David Hilbert has given a simple axiomatic justification for the theory of tautologies which enables us to derive

---

[1] A combination of proposition variables $A, B, C, \ldots$ by logical symbols is called a *logical formula*.

[2] An important representation of the fundamental problems and their solutions is given by Kleene, a first introduction by Meschkowski (2).

all tautologies from certain axioms and formal 'deduction rules'. The remarkable feature of this system is that the *freedom from contradiction* of the propositions thus deduced can easily be proved. Thus propositional calculus provides a simple model for a mathematical theory whose freedom from contradiction can be demonstrated. The corresponding propositions for other mathematical theories (*e.g.*, the formal theory of numbers) are essentially more difficult to prove.

We shall now show that elementary propositional calculus can also be interpreted in terms of lattice theory. To do this we observe that the propositions

$$A \wedge (A \vee B) \Leftrightarrow A \tag{17}$$

and

$$A \wedge B \Leftrightarrow B \wedge A \tag{18}$$

have the character of tautologies. According to (II, 10) the relation expressed by the symbol $\Leftrightarrow$ yields a proposition which is true if, and only if, the two propositions combined by the symbol have the same truth value. One can see at once that the proposition on the left hand side of the formula (17) is true if, and only if, A is true. The truth value of B is immaterial. Formula (18) expresses the fact that in combining two propositions A and B by the symbol $\wedge$, the sequence is of no importance.

But the propositions (17) and (18) correspond to the lattice axioms (3c) and (3a). One has only to replace the symbols $\sqcap$ and $\sqcup$ by $\wedge$ and $\vee$, and the equality sign by the logical symbol $\Leftrightarrow$. This result suggests an examination of the analogues of the remaining lattice axioms with respect to their tautological character. This shows that the logical formulae

$$A \wedge B \Leftrightarrow B \wedge A \tag{19a}$$

$$(A \wedge B) \wedge C \Leftrightarrow A \wedge (B \wedge C) \tag{19b}$$

$$A \wedge (A \vee B) \Leftrightarrow A \tag{19c}$$

$$A \vee B \Leftrightarrow B \vee A \tag{20a}$$

$$(A \vee B) \vee C \Leftrightarrow A \vee (B \vee C) \tag{20b}$$

$$A \vee (A \wedge B) \Leftrightarrow A \tag{20c}$$

are all tautologies. Hence it is possible to interpret the set $\{A\}$ of propositions $(A, B, C, \ldots)$ as a lattice in which the binary relations are given by the symbols $\wedge$ and $\vee$.

A special comment is necessary on the fact that the equality sign has here been replaced by the symbol ⇔. We note in this connection that the symbol ⇔ in propositional calculus has the character of an equivalence (see V 1); *i.e.*, the binary relation ⇔ is symmetric, reflexive, and transitive. In deriving the fundamental theorems of lattice theory (see VI 2) we made use only of the equivalence character of equality. Hence we can deduce the corresponding theorems for the set of propositions, since the conclusions are also valid for the sign ⇔.

We observe further that the distributive laws

$$A \vee (B \wedge C) \Leftrightarrow (A \vee B) \wedge (A \vee C) \tag{21}$$

and

$$A \wedge (B \vee C) \Leftrightarrow (A \wedge B) \vee (A \wedge C) \tag{22}$$

are also tautologies. We can show this in the usual way using Table (II, 10). Apart from this it is also possible to give a pictorial representation of combinations by logical symbols and of the validity of tautologies by means of *electrical circuits*.

Fig. 26 shows a wire that is broken by a switch *a*. We assume

FIG. 26.

that a voltage is applied across the ends of the wire. A current flows in the wire if, and only if, the proposition

A : *The switch a is closed*

is true. In a wire with two switches *a* and *b* arranged in series a current flows if, and only if, the proposition **A** ∧ **B** is true. Here **B** is the statement: *The switch b is closed*.

Fig. 27a can thus serve as an illustration of the logical sum **A** ∧ **B**. Through the parallel connection of Fig. 27b current will flow when *at least* one of the two switches is closed. This system symbolises the proposition **A** ∨ **B**.

FIG. 27a, b.

For the more complicated circuits that follow we shall admit that several switches may be designated by the same letter. We shall stipulate that switches with the same letter must be either all open or all closed.

Fig. 28 shows a series connection of a switch *a* with the parallel connection of two switches denoted by *a* and *b*. This connection

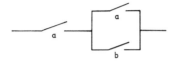

FIG. 28.

represents the proposition $A \wedge (A \vee B)$. According to our stipulation the switches designated by *a* are either both open or both closed. One can then see at once that a current flows in this combination if, and only if, *a* is closed, *i.e.*, proposition A is true. Whether B is true, *i.e.*, *b* is closed, is immaterial. Thus one can read from Fig. 28 the equivalence

$$A \wedge (A \vee B) \Leftrightarrow A$$

The arrangement of Fig. 29a symbolizes the proposition

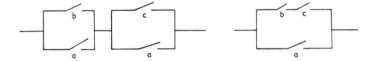

FIG. 29a, b.

$(A \vee B) \wedge (A \vee C)$. Since by our stipulation the two switches denoted by *a* are operated in the same way, we can obviously modify the arrangement so that the two switches are combined into one. This leads to the arrangement shown in Fig. 29b. Current will then flow through the arrangement of Fig. 29b only if this is possible also for the arrangement of Fig. 29a, and vice versa. Hence we have the equivalence

$$(A \vee B) \wedge (A \vee C) \Leftrightarrow A \vee (B \wedge C)$$

But this is our distributive law (21). The validity of the second distributive law (22) can be illustrated by Figs. 30a and 30b. Current flows through the arrangement of Fig. 30a if, and only if, it also flows through the arrangement of Fig. 30b.

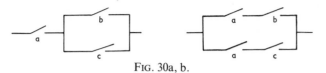

FIG. 30a, b.

One can extend still further the representation of logical formulae by switching circuits and also symbolize the implications in this manner. Since $A \Rightarrow B$ stands for $\neg A \vee B$, for the representation of this implication one need only introduce a 'negative' switch $\neg a$, which is open whenever a is closed, and vice versa.

We shall leave further games with electrical circuits to the reader! We confine ourselves to the statement that, in this way, the two distributive laws (21) and (22) can be represented pictorially. The proof is easy with the help of Table (II, 10).

Let us collect together our results:

The set $\{A\}$ of propositions $(A, B, C, \ldots)$ forms a distributive lattice, in which the binary relations $\sqcap$ and $\sqcup$ are given by the logical symbols $\wedge$ and $\vee$.

5. Projective geometry

If one projects the points of a line g from a point S on to a line h (which cuts g), then one obtains a one-to-one mapping of the points of g on to those of h (see Fig. 31).

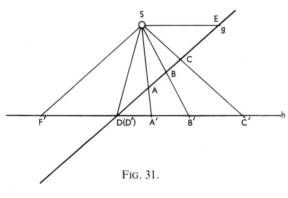

FIG. 31.

$$A \leftrightarrow A', \qquad B \leftrightarrow B', \qquad C \leftrightarrow C', \qquad D \leftrightarrow D' = D$$

One must note, however, that there are 'exceptional points'. If SE is parallel to h, then the point E has no image on the line h, and for the point F' on h (where SF' is parallel to g) there exists no point F on g having F' as its image.

If we want to formulate theorems about projections, such exceptional points are very awkward. In projective geometry one therefore introduces an 'improper' point, or a 'point at infinity', on every line. One can then say that any two lines of a plane intersect. They either have an ordinary point of intersection, or they are parallel, in which case they have a point at infinity in common. By introducing these points at infinity one can remove from the theorems of projective geometry limitations which would otherwise be necessary because of the exceptions.

Projective geometry can be based on axioms without the use of the concept of coordinates. But one can also proceed analytically. In *classical* analytical geometry, a point P in the plane is given by two coordinates (x, y), and a line by a linear equation

$$ax + by + c = 0 \tag{23}$$

If we put

$$x = \frac{x_1}{x_3}, \qquad y = \frac{x_2}{x_3} \tag{24}$$

then the equation (23) of the line assumes the form

$$ax_1 + bx_2 + cx_3 = 0 \tag{25}$$

and the point P is characterized by a system of three coordinates

$$P = \begin{pmatrix} x_1 \\ x_2 \\ x_3 \end{pmatrix} \tag{26}$$

It is assumed first that $x_3 \neq 0$. For every number triple (x_1, x_2, x_3) (with $x_3 \neq 0$) one can determine numbers x and y by (24) which can be interpreted as coordinates of a point in the (x, y)-plane. The system of numbers $(\lambda x_1, \lambda x_2, \lambda x_3)$ represents the same point as (x_1, x_2, x_3), and we can therefore put[1]

$$\begin{pmatrix} \lambda x_1 \\ \lambda x_2 \\ \lambda x_3 \end{pmatrix} = \begin{pmatrix} x_1 \\ x_2 \\ x_3 \end{pmatrix} \tag{27}$$

---

[1] All numbers used here are assumed to be rational. This suffices for linear geometry. We shall consider the theory of real numbers later in Chapter VIII. We remark here, however, that all the propositions of linear projective geometry remain valid if real numbers are taken for the coordinates and coefficients.

We shall now admit also triples (26) for which $x_3 = 0$, but $\sum\limits_{\nu=1}^{3} x_\nu^2$ is not equal to zero. The triples (26) are called the *points of the projective plane*. The points with $x_3 = 0$ are the *points at infinity*.

It is now possible to state that any two lines of a plane have a point in common. The two parallel lines

$$ax + by + c = 0$$
$$ax + by + d = 0 \tag{28}$$

(where $c \neq d$) have no point in common according to classical geometry. But if we write the two equations (28) in homogeneous form we have

$$ax_1 + bx_2 + cx_3 = 0$$
$$ax_1 + bx_2 + dx_3 = 0 \tag{28'}$$

and these two lines of the projective plane have the point at infinity

$$U = \begin{pmatrix} -b \\ a \\ 0 \end{pmatrix}$$

in common.

There is yet another way of expressing a line in the projective plane in analytical form. Let

$$U = \begin{pmatrix} u_1 \\ u_2 \\ u_3 \end{pmatrix}, \qquad V = \begin{pmatrix} v_1 \\ v_2 \\ v_3 \end{pmatrix}$$

be two arbitrary points of the plane. Then the points given by

$$X = \begin{pmatrix} x_1 \\ x_2 \\ x_3 \end{pmatrix} = \lambda \cdot U + \mu \cdot V \qquad (\lambda^2 + \mu^2 \neq 0) \tag{29}$$

lie on a line. For it follows from (29) that the determinant formed by the coordinates of the points U, V, and X vanishes:[1] *i.e.*,

$$D = \begin{vmatrix} x_1 & x_2 & x_3 \\ u_1 & u_2 & u_3 \\ v_1 & v_2 & v_3 \end{vmatrix} = 0 \tag{30}$$

[1] See, for example, Peschl.

Expanding this determinant by the first row, one obtains a homogeneous linear equation

$$x_1 . \alpha + x_2 . \beta + x_3 . \gamma = 0 \tag{31}$$

where the numbers α, β, and γ are minors of (30). (31) is again the equation of a line in homogeneous form.

The method shown here for the plane can be extended to three-dimensional space.

The points of the three-dimensional projective space[1] are given by the number quadruples

$$X = \begin{pmatrix} x_1 \\ x_2 \\ x_3 \\ x_4 \end{pmatrix}, \qquad \sum_{v=1}^{4} x_v^2 \neq 0 \tag{32}$$

Points for which $x_4 = 0$ are called points at infinity. The linear combinations of two quadruples

$$X = \begin{pmatrix} x_1 \\ x_2 \\ x_3 \\ x_4 \end{pmatrix} = \lambda \begin{pmatrix} u_1 \\ u_2 \\ u_3 \\ u_4 \end{pmatrix} + \mu \begin{pmatrix} v_1 \\ v_2 \\ v_3 \\ v_4 \end{pmatrix}$$

again give the points of a line. The combinations of *three* points (which do not lie in a line) give a plane

$$X = \begin{pmatrix} x_1 \\ x_2 \\ x_3 \\ x_4 \end{pmatrix} = \lambda \begin{pmatrix} u_1 \\ u_2 \\ u_3 \\ u_4 \end{pmatrix} + \mu \begin{pmatrix} v_1 \\ v_2 \\ v_3 \\ v_4 \end{pmatrix} + v \begin{pmatrix} w_1 \\ w_2 \\ w_3 \\ w_4 \end{pmatrix} \tag{33}$$

$$= \lambda U + \mu V + v W$$

[1] There is also a projective geometry in a space of n dimensions.

From (33) it follows that the determinant formed by the co-ordinates of the points X, U, V, and W vanishes: *i.e.*

$$D = \begin{vmatrix} x_1 & x_2 & x_3 & x_4 \\ u_1 & u_2 & u_3 & u_4 \\ v_1 & v_2 & v_3 & v_4 \\ w_1 & w_2 & w_3 & w_4 \end{vmatrix} = 0 \qquad (34)$$

Expanding by the first row again gives a homogeneous linear equation, the equation of the plane given by (33)

$$x_1 . a + x_2 . b + x_3 . c + x_4 . d = 0 \qquad (34')$$

It is easy to show that two planes always have a line in common. If the planes are parallel, the line consists entirely of points at infinity.

We shall now show that projective geometry can also be interpreted in terms of lattice theory.[1] To do this we denote the points of the three-dimensional projective space $R_{(3)}$ by P, Q, R, ..., the lines by $g, h, k, \ldots$, and the planes defined as linear combinations of three non-linear points by α, β, γ, ... We then define the set $L_{(3)}$ of the linear subspaces of $R_{(3)}$, consisting of the following elements:[2]

  a) the points,
  b) the lines,
  c) the planes of the space $R_{(3)}$,
  d) the whole projective space $R_{(3)}$ and the empty set.

We have already defined lines, planes as linear combinations of two, three points respectively. We can now interpret the empty set, the points, the whole space $R_{(3)}$ as linear combinations of 0, 1, 4 (non-coplanar) points respectively. These linear combinations of points are called *linear subspaces*.

In the set $L_{(3)}$ binary operations expressed by the symbols $\sqcap$ and $\sqcup$ are defined as follows:

---

[1] For the analytical development of projective geometry see, for example, Blaschke.

[2] The elements of $L_{(3)}$ are denoted by $p, q, r, \ldots$. In the special case of points we write $P, Q, R, \ldots$, for lines $g, h, k, \ldots$, etc.

If p and q are any elements of the set $L_{(3)}$ then

> $p \sqcap q$ is the largest linear subspace of $R_{(3)}$
> that wholly belongs to p and to q,
> $p \sqcup q$ is the smallest linear subspace to
> which p and q belong. $\hspace{2cm}$ (35)

Let us consider a few examples.

Let g and h be two lines lying in a plane α, with point of intersection P. Then

$$g \sqcap h = P, \qquad g \sqcup h = \alpha$$

If on the other hand g and h are skew,[1] then we have

$$g \sqcap h = \varnothing, \qquad g \sqcup h = R_{(3)}$$

For two planes α and β with the line of intersection g,

$$\alpha \sqcap \beta = g, \qquad \alpha \sqcup \beta = R_{(3)}$$

For two different points P and Q (which determine the line g) we have

$$P \sqcap Q = \varnothing, \qquad P \sqcup Q = g$$

It is easy to convince oneself that the lattice axioms are satisfied for the binary relations defined in this way. Hence we have the theorem:

The set $L_{(3)}$ of the linear subspaces of the three-dimensional projective space $R_{(3)}$ forms a lattice, in which the binary relations $\sqcap$ and $\sqcup$ are defined by (35).

We may still add that this lattice is *atomic*. A lattice is called atomic if it possesses *atoms*; these are the *upper neighbours of the null element*.

Not every lattice has a null element, and not every lattice with a null element also has atoms. An example is given by the set Q' of non-negative rational numbers with the binary relations

$$u \sqcap v = \mathrm{Max}(u, v), \qquad u \sqcup v = \mathrm{Min}(u, v)$$

This lattice has the number zero as null element. But there are no atoms since the number zero has no upper neighbours. Between zero and any positive rational number there always exists another rational number. On the other hand, the lattices represented in Figs. 20 and 22, for example, are atomic. In the lattice formed by the group G_3, the subgroups U_1, U_2, U_3, and U_4 are atoms, and

---

[1] Two lines which do not lie in a plane are called *skew*.

for the lattice represented by Fig. 22, the atoms are the prime numbers 2, 3, and 5.

In the lattice formed by the linear subspaces of $R_{(3)}$, the points are clearly the atoms. They are the upper neighbours of the empty set. Hence we have here an atomic lattice with infinitely many atoms.

For further properties of this lattice we refer the reader to the specialist literature. Our purpose was to show, by a few examples taken from quite different fields, the fruitfulness of lattice theory. The general theorems of this theory can be interpreted as propositions of set geometry, of propositional calculus, of elementary number theory, of the theory of subgroups, and of projective geometry. In particular the *principle of duality* holds in all these disciplines. This principle has long been known in projective geometry. We are now in a position to recognize it as a principle of a general mathematical structure.

6. Problems

1. Draw the graph of the number 770.
2. Show that for lattices the distributive law (9) follows from (10), and conversely.
3. Fig. 32 shows a number of partially ordered sets. Which of these are also lattices?

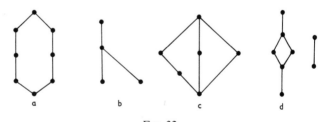

FIG. 32.

4. Draw the graphs of all lattices that contain exactly 5 elements.
5. In the set K of complex numbers $z = x + iy$, with rational x and y, a partial ordering is defined as follows

$$z = x + iy \ \mathbf{u} \ Z = x + iY, \quad \text{if } y \leqslant Y$$

   a) Does this partially ordered set possess minimal or maximal elements?

b) What additional condition will change this partially ordered set into a chain?

6. Which of the following logical formulae are tautologies?

a) $X \Rightarrow (Y \Rightarrow (X \wedge Y))$
b) $\neg A \Rightarrow (A \wedge B)$
c) $[A \wedge (A \Rightarrow B)] \Rightarrow B$
d) $X \vee (Y \wedge Z) \Rightarrow (X \vee Z)$

7. Determine whether the lattice of linear subspaces introduced in VI 5 is distributive.

CHAPTER SEVEN

Spaces

1. Metric spaces

During the last decade many books have been written about the problem of space. There was good justification for this. The conceptions of the philosophers (even Kant's notion of space) were questioned by modern theories of physicists and astronomers. Already the justification of a 'noneuclidean' geometry in the nineteenth century was sufficient reason to raise anew the question as to the nature of space.

It is not our task here to enter into the question of the 'real existence' of a euclidean or a noneuclidean geometry.[1] Even Einstein's ideas about the curvature of space caused by the distribution of matter cannot be the topic of this 'Introduction'.

We want to awaken an understanding of mathematical structures. For such considerations a space is a structure similar to the group or the lattice. Under certain assumptions a set M is called a space. The properties of this space can then be deduced from the axioms that hold for the space (the set M). The question, which is certainly interesting, whether such a mathematical structure is suitable for the description of certain physical observations, can be left aside in an introductory treatment dealing with the 'pure' mathematics.

There is, of course, a certain connection between the notation of the mathematical structure and its applications. The mathematician calls a set M a space precisely when it possesses certain properties with which we are familiar from physical space. For the further development of the theory, no reference is made to intuition, but only to the axioms of the structure and the consequences that may be deduced from them.

We shall begin with the definition of a space for which the possibility of measuring 'distances' is made the basis of the axioms.

---

[1] See, for example, Meschkowski (2), Chapter VIII.

A set M (with elements x, y, z, ...) is called a metric space if, for any two elements $x \in M$ and $y \in M$, there exists a non-negative real[1] number $D(x, y)$ having the following properties:

$$D(x, x) = 0 \tag{1a}$$

$$D(x, y) = D(y, x) > 0 \quad \text{for } x \neq y \tag{1b}$$

$$D(x, y) \leqslant D(x, z) + D(z, y) \tag{1c}$$

The elements of M are called the *points* of the space and the number $D(x, y)$ the *distance* of the points x and y.

The inequality (1c) is called the *triangle inequality*. The reason for this name will be understood if we consider as our first example of a metric space the space E of the points of a euclidean plane. Let x, y and z be any three points of E, $D(x, y)$ the length of the line segment (x, y). If x has coordinates x_1, x_2 in a rectangular Cartesian coordinate system, and y the coordinates y_1, y_2, then the distance $D(x, y)$ is given by

$$D(x, y) = +\sqrt{(x_1 - y_1)^2 + (x_2 - y_2)^2} \tag{2}$$

The inequality (1c), which can easily be verified for this definition of distance, can then be interpreted thus: *the sum of the lengths of two sides of a triangle can never be less than the third side.*

One can easily see that the following sets are also metric spaces.

(A). The set of complex numbers $z = x + iy$ with the distance

$$D(z_1, z_2) = |z_1 - z_2| \tag{3}$$

(B). The set of number triples

$$x = \begin{pmatrix} x_1 \\ x_2 \\ x_3 \end{pmatrix}$$

of real numbers x_1, x_2, x_3 and the distance

$$D(x, y) = +\sqrt{\sum_{k=1}^{3} (x_k - y_k)^2} \tag{4}$$

[1] In some examples we assume the existence of the real numbers to be known. A theory of these numbers will be given in Chapter VIII.

(C). The set Q of rational numbers $(u, v, w, \ldots)$; here the distance is given by

$$D(u, v) = |u - v| \qquad (5)$$

For the examples given so far there is an easy geometrical interpretation of distance. But this is not required by our definition of distance. We shall therefore give a further example of a metric space in which such a geometrical interpretation of distance is not immediately evident.

(D). The set $Q^{(3)}$ of triples of rational numbers

$$x = \begin{pmatrix} x_1 \\ x_2 \\ x_3 \end{pmatrix}$$

with the distance

$$D(x, y) = \sum_{k=1}^{3} \frac{|x_k - y_k|}{1 + |x_k - y_k|} \qquad (6)$$

One can see at once that the distance so defined has the properties (1a) and (1b). The proof of the triangle inequality is as follows:

For $k = 1, 2$ and 3 we have

$$\frac{|x_k - y_k|}{1 + |x_k - y_k|} + \frac{|y_k - z_k|}{1 + |y_k - z_k|} \geqslant \frac{|x_k - y_k| + |y_k - z_k|}{1 + |x_k - y_k| + |y_k - z_k|} = \frac{a}{1 + a} \qquad (7)$$

where

$$a = |x_k - y_k| + |y_k - z_k|$$

Now from $a \geqslant b \geqslant 0$ it follows that

$$a + ab \geqslant b + ab$$

and hence

$$\frac{a}{1 + a} \geqslant \frac{b}{1 + b} \qquad (8)$$

Since

$$|x_k - y_k| + |y_k - z_k| \geqslant |x_k - z_k|$$

we deduce from (7) and (8) that

$$\frac{|x_k - y_k|}{1 + |x_k - y_k|} + \frac{|y_k - z_k|}{1 + |y_k - z_k|} \geqslant \frac{|x_k - z_k|}{1 + |x_k - z_k|}$$

By definition (6) we therefore have

$$D(x, y) + D(y, z) \geqslant D(x, x)$$

(E). For the reader acquainted with the elementary theory of sequences,[1] we shall add the following example of a metric space. Let H be the set of sequences

$$x = \{x_1, x_2, x_3, \ldots\}$$

of real numbers x_ν, for which

$$\sum_{\nu=1}^{\infty} x_\nu^2 = x_1^2 + x_2^2 + x_3^2 + \ldots$$

is convergent. These sequences are called points of the *Hilbert space* H. The distance $D(x, y)$ of two points of this space is given by

$$(D(x, y))^2 = \sum_{\nu=1}^{\infty} (x_\nu - y_\nu)^2 \qquad (9)$$

It is easy to see that the series (9) converges if $\sum x_\nu^2$ and $\sum y_\nu^2$ converge. For, from $(x_\nu - y_\nu)^2 \geqslant 0$ it follows that

$$2x_\nu \cdot y_\nu \leqslant x_\nu^2 + y_\nu^2$$

and hence $\sum x_\nu \cdot y_\nu$ converges if $\sum x_\nu^2 < \infty$, $\sum y_\nu^2 < \infty$. The convergence of (9) follows from this. Since the triangle inequality (1c) holds for the distance defined by (9), the set H (with the distance (9)), is indeed a metric space.

2. Topological spaces

In VII 1 we characterized the space by its metric. The measuring of distances is, however, by no means the only way of obtaining a clear picture of a space. The space of our perception is distinguished from other sets, in that to every point of the space there belong certain sets of points which one can call 'neighbourhoods' of the point. The concept of such a structure of space is independent of the possibility of measuring. One can put these perceptual properties of a 'neighbourhood' on an axiomatic basis and in this way create a new and more general concept of space.

---

[1] See, for example, Meschkowski (6).

Definition. A set M is called a topological space if for each element $a \in M$ there exists at least one subset $U(a) \subset M$ (called a neighbourhood of a) having the following properties:

T1) *Each element a is contained as an element in each of its neighbourhoods $U(a)$; i.e., $a \in U(a)$.*

T2) *For two neighbourhoods $U_1(a)$ and $U_2(a)$ there always exists a neighbourhood $V(a)$ which is contained in the intersection of $U_1(a)$ and $U_2(a)$; i.e., $V(a) \subset U_1(a) \cap U_2(a)$.*

T3) *If b is an element of a neighbourhood $U(a)$, then there exists at least one neighbourhood $U(b)$ which is contained in $U(a)$; i.e., $U(b) \subset U(a)$.*

The elements of such a topological space are called *points*.

We have already met examples of topological spaces. Obviously *all metric spaces R are also topological spaces.* For this interpretation we have to give a suitable definition of the neighbourhood of a point $a \in R$. This can be done as follows.

A neighbourhood $U(a)$ is a set of points $b \in R$ for which the distance $D(a, b) < k$.

For the three-dimensional euclidean space (example (B) of VII 1) these neighbourhoods are the interior points of spheres with centre a and radius k. In the metric space Q (example (C) of VII 1) the neighbourhoods are the symmetric intervals $]a-k, a+k[$.

It is clear that with this definition of neighbourhood all metric spaces become topological spaces. One has only to convince oneself that the properties T1), T2), and T3) are satisfied. T1) is satisfied, since $D(a, a) = 0 < k$ for all positive numbers k. If $U_1(a)$ and $U_2(a)$ are the neighbourhoods which belong to the numbers k_1 and k_2 ($k_1 < k_2$), then $U_1(a) \subset U_2(a)$, $U_1(a) \cap U_2(a) = U_1(a)$, and one can simply put $V(a) = U_1(a)$. Lastly the validity of T3 can be deduced from the triangle inequality (1c). Let $U(a)$ be the neighbourhood of a given by $D(a, x) < k$. Now let $b \in U(a)$, so that $D(a, b) = k_1 < k$. We now define a neighbourhood $U(b)$ by $D(b, y) < k_2$ with $k_1 + k_2 < k$. By the triangle inequality we then have

$$D(a, y) \leqslant D(a, b) + D(b, y) < k_1 + k_2 < k$$

But this means that *all points y of the neighbourhood $U(b)$ also belong to the neighbourhood $U(a)$: i.e., $U(b) \subset U(a)$.*

In Fig. 33 the neighbourhood $U(a)$ is shown as a circle. Note, however, that in the proof no special assumption was made about the neighbourhood except the triangle inequality (1c), secured by the axiom.

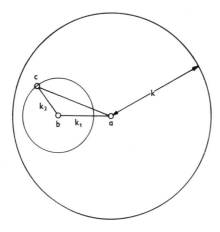

FIG. 33.

Hence every metric space can also be interpreted as a topological space. However, there exist topological spaces for which no metric is defined, as the following two examples show.

(F). *Every arbitrary set M (with elements $a, b, c, \ldots$) can be interpreted as a topological space.*

One need only ascribe to every element $a \in M$ the set $\{a\}$ as neighbourhood, where $\{a\}$ is the set which contains only the one element a. Then obviously $a \in \{a\}$. Since, according to our definition, only *at least* one neighbourhood must be defined for each element a, T1) is satisfied. The statements T2) and T3) do not apply, since there are no further neighbourhoods and the neighbourhood $U(a)$ contains no point other than a.

(G). Let K_ρ be the set of complex numbers $r + is$ with rational r and s. To a number $\rho = r + is \in K_\rho$ we ascribe neighbourhoods $U(r, \varepsilon)$, consisting of the sets of numbers $r_1 + i\sigma$ for which $|r - r_1| < \varepsilon$. These neighbourhoods thus form parallel strips of width 2ε, having the line $x = r$ as axis of symmetry.

One can see at once that, for these neighbourhoods, conditions T1), T2), and T3) are satisfied. K_ρ with these neighbourhoods is therefore a topological space. In this space all neighbourhoods of a point $P_1 = r + is_1$ are also neighbourhoods of $P_2 = r + is_2$ (see Fig. 34).

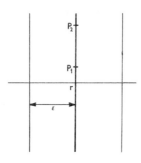

FIG. 34.

A topological space R is called *separable* (or also a *Hausdorff space*) if it satisfies the following condition:

T4) *For any two different points a and b of the space R there always exist neighbourhoods U(a) and U(b) whose intersection is empty*

$$U(a) \cap U(b) = \varnothing$$

Clearly the topological space defined in (G) is not separable. On the other hand all *metric spaces* are separable, if the neighbourhood is defined by means of the metric. If a and b are two different points of such a space and if $D(a, b) = k$, then the neighbourhoods defined by $D(a, x) < \frac{1}{3}k$ and $D(b, y) < \frac{1}{3}k$ certainly have no element in common. This can be shown at once with the help of the triangle inequality.

3. Definition of a filter

In classical analysis problems such as the determination of tangents, the calculation of areas, etc., are based on operations with convergent number sequences. For the treatment of similar problems in general topological spaces it is necessary to introduce a suitable generalization of the concept of a sequence. It will be shown that the concept of a *filter*, which is suitable for this purpose, is useful not only for general topology. Some proofs in classical analysis can also be formulated much more simply by means of the filter concept. In this introduction the filter concept will be used mainly as a basis for the theory of the real numbers.

Definition.[1] *Let M be an arbitrary set. A set $\mathfrak{F}$ of subsets of M is called a filter (on M) if it has the following properties:*

F1) $\phi \notin \mathfrak{F}$,

F2) $\mathfrak{F} \neq \phi$,

F3) *If $A \in \mathfrak{F}$ and $B \in \mathfrak{F}$, then there exists a $C \in \mathfrak{F}$, which is contained in the intersection of A and B*

$$C \subset A \cap B$$

In particular, the condition F3) is fulfilled if the intersection of any two sets of $\mathfrak{F}$ always belongs to $\mathfrak{F}$.

It follows from the definition that the power set $P(M)$ *is not a filter*, since it contains the empty set as an element. We shall now give a few examples of filters.

(I). Let $\{a_n\}$ be an arbitrary infinite sequence of numbers $\{a_1, a_2, a_3, \ldots\}$ and $\mathfrak{F}_1$ the sequence of remainders, *i.e.*,

$$\mathfrak{F}_1 = \{r_1, r_2, r_3, \ldots\},$$

where

$$r_n = \{a_{n+1}, a_{n+2}, a_{n+3}, \ldots\}$$

The sequence $\mathfrak{F}_1$ of remainders is clearly a filter.

(II). Let $\mathfrak{F}_2$ be the set of all rectangles in the (x, y)-plane having their sides parallel to the axes and containing a fixed point P as an interior point (see Fig. 35). By 'rectangle' is meant here the *set of*

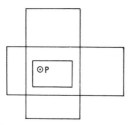

FIG. 35.

all interior points of a right-angled parallelogram. The intersection of two such rectangles with sides parallel to the axes is clearly again a rectangle with the same property. One can see at once from this that $\mathfrak{F}_2$ has the property F3).

---

[1] Bourbaki uses *filter basis* for filter. The filter in the sense of Bourbaki (which is not used here) is often called a Bourbaki-filter in the newer literature.

(III). The set of open squares $0 < x < a$, $0 < y < a$ forms a filter $\mathfrak{F}_3$ on the topological space in which the distance is defined by (2) (see Fig. 36).

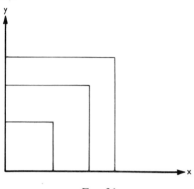

FIG. 36.

(IV). Let $\mathfrak{F}_4$ be the set of open intervals $]a, b[$ on the set R of real numbers, which contain the closed interval $[0, 1]$. This set of sets is also a filter (see Fig. 37).

FIG. 37.

(V). Let $\mathfrak{F}_5$ be the set of bounded and convex[1] regions of a plane ε, which have as boundary a continuous simple closed curve, and which contain a fixed point $P \in \varepsilon$ as an interior point. Since the intersection of any two such regions always belongs to $\mathfrak{F}_5$, this set of sets is also a filter (see Fig. 38).

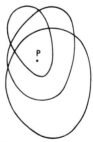

FIG. 38.

[1] A region is called *bounded* if it lies entirely in the interior of a circle. It is *convex* if, for any two points P and Q lying in the region, the whole line segment PQ also belongs to the region.

As a counter example, note that the set of the boundary curves of the regions of $\mathfrak{F}_5$ do *not* form a filter. For the intersection of two such curves can be empty. Hence the set of curves does not possess the filter property F3).

All the examples of filters considered so far were sets of sets with *infinitely many elements*. This, however, is not required by the definition. Indeed there are filters on finite sets with a finite number of elements.

(VI). Let M_6 be the set $\{1, 2, 3, 4, 5\}$, $\mathfrak{F}_6$ the set of subsets

$$\{1\}, \{1, 2\}, \{1, 3, 4\}, \{1, 4, 5\}$$

This set $\mathfrak{F}_6$ is a filter on M_6. The intersection of any two of these sets always contains the element 1. Hence the set $\{1\}$ is a subset of all the intersections of sets from M_6.

On the other hand, the set $\mathfrak{G}_6$ of subsets

$$\{1\}, \{1, 3, 4\}, \{1, 2\}, \{3, 4, 5\}$$

of M_6 is *not* a filter, since the intersection of the last two sets is empty.

(VII). Finally we shall note that a filter can be defined on every non-empty set M. This is the filter $\{M\}$, which contains only the single element M. According to our convention about the meaning of the bracket $\{\ \}$, $\{M\}$ is the set with the *one* element M. This set is not empty, nor does it contain the empty set as an element. Finally F3) is trivially satisfied, since our filter contains only one element.

4. Relations between filters

A filter $\mathfrak{F}$ is called a refinement of the filter $\mathfrak{G}$ (written $\mathfrak{F} \lhd \mathfrak{G}$), if for every element $G \in \mathfrak{G}$ there exists an element $F \in \mathfrak{F}$ which is contained in G

$$\mathfrak{F} \lhd \mathfrak{G} \Leftrightarrow \mathsf{V} G\, (G \in \mathfrak{G}) \Rightarrow \exists F\, (F \subset G \wedge F \in \mathfrak{F}) \tag{10}$$

Since the relation of inclusion ($\subset$) is *reflexive* and *transitive*, so also will be the refinement relation between filters. Hence we have

$$\mathfrak{F} \lhd \mathfrak{F} \tag{11}$$

and

$$(\mathfrak{F} \lhd \mathfrak{G}) \wedge (\mathfrak{G} \lhd \mathfrak{H}) \Rightarrow \mathfrak{F} \lhd \mathfrak{H} \tag{12}$$

Let us consider a few examples.

(I). The set Q of rational numbers is converted into a topological space[1] by defining a neighbourhood for its elements $r \in Q$. We shall regard the open intervals $]r-q, r+q[$ $(q \in Q)$ as neighbourhoods. The set of these intervals is clearly a filter; it is the *neighbourhood filter* $\mathfrak{U}(r)$ for the rational number r.

We now define two further filters $\mathfrak{U}_1(r)$ and $\mathfrak{U}_2(r)$ as follows:

$\mathfrak{U}_1(r)$ is the set of open intervals from Q, which contain r as an interior point.

$\mathfrak{U}_2(r)$ is the set of intervals

$$\left]r-\frac{1}{n}, r+\frac{1}{n}\right[, \qquad n = 1, 2, 3, \ldots$$

Clearly the set $\mathfrak{U}(r)$ of symmetric intervals is a subset of $\mathfrak{U}_1(r)$, and the set $\mathfrak{U}_2(r)$ is a subset of $\mathfrak{U}(r)$.

Each of the three filters $\mathfrak{U}(r)$, $\mathfrak{U}_1(r)$, and $\mathfrak{U}_2(r)$ is a refinement of each of the other two. We shall confine ourselves to the proof that $\mathfrak{U}_2(r) \lhd \mathfrak{U}_1(r)$. For this we have only to note that every interval $]s, t[$ which contains r as an interior point also contains an interval

$$\left]r-\frac{1}{n}, r+\frac{1}{n}\right[$$

as a subset. One only has to choose a sufficiently large number n.

(II). Let $\mathfrak{F}_3$ be the filter of open squares defined in VII 3 under (III) and $\mathfrak{F}_3^*$ the set of open circles $x^2 + y^2 < r^2$, $r > 0$. Clearly $\mathfrak{F}_3^*$ is a filter, and we have

$$\mathfrak{F}_3 \lhd \mathfrak{F}_3^*, \tag{13}$$

for in each of the circles, no matter how small r is, there is always a square of the filter $\mathfrak{F}_3$. The converse of (13) obviously does not hold, for none of the circular discs $x^2 + y^2 < r^2$ is a subset of any of the squares.

(III). Let M be the set $\{1, 2, 3, 4, 5\}$. On M there are the two filters

$$\mathfrak{F}' = \{\{1\}, \{1, 2, 3\}, M\}$$

$$\mathfrak{F}'' = \{\{1, 2\}, \{1, 2, 4\}, \{1, 2, 4, 5\}\}$$

Clearly $\mathfrak{F}' \lhd \mathfrak{F}''$, since the set $\{1\}$ is a subset of all the sets belonging to $\mathfrak{F}''$. On the other hand $\mathfrak{F}'' \lhd \mathfrak{F}'$ is not true, since none of the sets of $\mathfrak{F}''$ is a subset of $\{1\}$.

---

[1]This space is also called the rational topology.

(IV). The remainders of the sequence $\{n^{-1}\}$ form a filter

$$\Re_n = \left\{\left\{\frac{1}{n+1}, \frac{1}{n+2}, \frac{1}{n+3}, \ldots\right\}\right\}, \qquad n = 1, 2, 3, \ldots$$

which is a refinement of the filter of the intervals

$$\Im_n = \left\{\left]-\frac{1}{n}, +\frac{1}{n}\right[\right\} \tag{14}$$

But $\Im_n$ is obviously not a refinement of $\Re_n$.

Definition. Two filters $\Im$ and $\mathfrak{G}$ are called equivalent (written $\sim$) if both $\Im \lhd \mathfrak{G}$ and $\mathfrak{G} \lhd \Im$

$$\Im \sim \mathfrak{G} \Leftrightarrow (\Im \lhd \mathfrak{G}) \wedge (\mathfrak{G} \lhd \Im) \tag{15}$$

According to this definition the filters $\mathfrak{U}(r)$, $\mathfrak{U}_1(r)$ and $\mathfrak{U}_2(r)$ introduced in (I) are equivalent.

$$\mathfrak{U}(r) \sim \mathfrak{U}_1(r), \qquad \mathfrak{U}_1(r) \sim \mathfrak{U}_2(r), \qquad \mathfrak{U}(r) \sim \mathfrak{U}_2(r)$$

However the refinement relations of the remaining examples are not reversible. But it is easy to find filters equivalent to these. For the filter $\Im_3^*$ defined in (II), for example, the filter $\Im_3^{**}$ of squares[1] with centre the origin and sides parallel to the axes is equivalent (see Fig. 39). Clearly $\Im_3^* \lhd \Im_3^{**}$ and $\Im_3^{**} \lhd \Im_3^*$, so that $\Im_3^* \sim \Im_3^{**}$.

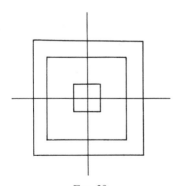

FIG. 39.

Incidentally this filter is also equivalent to the filter $\Im_2$ (Example (II) of VII 3), if P is chosen as the origin.

We note further that the equivalence relation defined here for filters evidently possesses the characteristic properties of this type

---

[1] 'Square' stands here for the set of interior points of a right-angled rhombus.

of relation (see III 6): it is *symmetric, reflexive,* and *transitive.*

$$\mathfrak{F} \sim \mathfrak{G} \Leftrightarrow \mathfrak{G} \sim \mathfrak{F}, \qquad \mathfrak{F} \sim \mathfrak{F}$$
$$(\mathfrak{F}_1 \sim \mathfrak{F}_2) \wedge (\mathfrak{F}_2 \sim \mathfrak{F}_3) \Rightarrow \mathfrak{F}_1 \sim \mathfrak{F}_3 \tag{16}$$

Given two filters $\mathfrak{F}$ and $\mathfrak{G}$ on a set M one can form (just as in the case of any two sets) the intersection $\mathfrak{F} \cap \mathfrak{G}$. According to the definition of II 3 this is the set of subsets of M that belong both to $\mathfrak{F}$ and to $\mathfrak{G}$. Note that this intersection must be distinguished from the set $\mathfrak{F} \sqcap \mathfrak{G}$, which is defined by[1]

$$\mathfrak{F} \sqcap \mathfrak{G} = \{F \cap G / F \in \mathfrak{F} \wedge G \in \mathfrak{G}\} \tag{17}$$

$\mathfrak{F} \cap \mathfrak{G}$ is thus the intersection of $\mathfrak{F}$ and $\mathfrak{G}$, but $\mathfrak{F} \sqcap \mathfrak{G}$ is the set of the intersections of sets belonging to $\mathfrak{F}$ and $\mathfrak{G}$. By F1) and F2), $\mathfrak{F} \sqcap \mathfrak{G}$ is certainly not a filter if it contains at least one empty intersection $F \cap G$. Otherwise $\mathfrak{F} \sqcap \mathfrak{G}$ is again a filter.

The set of sets $\mathfrak{F} \sqcap \mathfrak{G}$ defined by (17) is a filter if, and only if, none of the sets $F \cap G$ is empty. This filter is called the intersection filter of $\mathfrak{F}$ and $\mathfrak{G}$.

To prove this theorem we have to show that F3) is satisfied for $\mathfrak{F} \sqcap \mathfrak{G}$. The validity of F1) and F2) follows directly from the assumptions. Let

$$F_1 \in \mathfrak{F}, \qquad F_2 \in \mathfrak{F}, \qquad G_1 \in \mathfrak{G}, \qquad G_2 \in \mathfrak{G}$$

Then

$$F_1 \cap G_1 \in \mathfrak{F} \sqcap \mathfrak{G}, \qquad F_2 \cap G_2 \in \mathfrak{F} \sqcap \mathfrak{G}$$

We have to show that the intersection $(F_1 \cap G_1) \cap (F_2 \cap G_2)$ contains an element of $\mathfrak{F} \sqcap \mathfrak{G}$.

Because of the filter properties of $\mathfrak{F}$ and $\mathfrak{G}$ there exist non-empty sets F_3 and G_3 with the property

$$F_3 \in \mathfrak{F}, \qquad G_3 \in \mathfrak{G}, \qquad F_3 \subset F_1,$$
$$F_3 \subset F_2, \qquad G_3 \subset G_1, \qquad G_3 \subset G_2 \tag{18}$$

By (18), $F_3 \cap G_3 \in \mathfrak{F} \sqcap \mathfrak{F}$, and moreover we have

$$(F_3 \cap G_3) \subset (F_1 \cap G_1), \qquad (F_3 \cap G_3) \subset (F_2 \cap G_2)$$

so that

$$(F_3 \cap G_3) \subset (F_1 \cap G_1) \cap (F_2 \cap G_2)$$

Hence the filter properties of $\mathfrak{F} \sqcap \mathfrak{G}$ are established.

---

[1] We use here the sign that we used for lattices with the meaning defined by (17).

As an example consider on Q the filters

$$\mathfrak{F} = \left\{ \left] -\frac{1}{2n}, +\frac{1}{2n} \right[\right\}, \qquad \mathfrak{G} = \left\{ \left] -\frac{1}{2n-1}, +\frac{1}{2n-1} \right[\right\}$$

$$n = 1, 2, 3, \ldots$$

Since none of the intervals of $\mathfrak{F}$ is also an interval of $\mathfrak{G}$, the intersection $\mathfrak{F} \cap \mathfrak{G}$ is empty. On the other hand

$$\mathfrak{F} \sqcap \mathfrak{G} = \left\{ \left] -\frac{1}{n}, +\frac{1}{n} \right[\right\}, \qquad n = 2, 3, 4, \ldots$$

is a filter.

By analogy with $\mathfrak{F} \sqcap \mathfrak{G}$ we can define the *union filter* $\mathfrak{F} \sqcup \mathfrak{G}$ by

$$\mathfrak{F} \sqcup \mathfrak{G} = \{ F \cup G / F \in \mathfrak{F} \wedge G \in \mathfrak{G} \}$$

The demonstration of the filter properties of $\mathfrak{F} \sqcup \mathfrak{G}$ is left to the reader. We shall only remark that it is important to distinguish $\mathfrak{F} \sqcup \mathfrak{G}$ from the union $\mathfrak{F} \cup \mathfrak{G}$. $\mathfrak{F} \sqcup \mathfrak{G}$ is the set of the unions of elements of $\mathfrak{F}$ with elements of $\mathfrak{G}$, whilst $\mathfrak{F} \cup \mathfrak{G}$ is the union of the sets $\mathfrak{F}$ and $\mathfrak{G}$.

5. Convergence of filters

Definition. A filter $\mathfrak{F}$ in a topological space T is said to converge to a point $a \in T$ if it is a refinement of the neighbourhood filter $\mathfrak{U}(a)$.

Since for every filter $\mathfrak{F}$ the relation $\mathfrak{F} \vartriangleleft \mathfrak{F}$ holds, it follows in particular that the neighbourhood filter $\mathfrak{U}(a)$ converges to a. One writes

$$\lim \mathfrak{U}(a) = a \tag{19}$$

Many readers will be familiar with the concept of convergence from the theory of number sequences.[1] It will therefore be useful if we first apply our definition to filters of 'remainders' of sequences of numbers (Example (I) of VII 3).

In differential calculus it is customary to define convergence of a sequence $\{a_n\}$ as follows:

The sequence $\{a_n\}$ is said to converge to the limit a, if for every $\varepsilon > 0$ there exists a number $N(\varepsilon)$ such that

$$|a_n - a| < \varepsilon \tag{20}$$

for $n > N(\varepsilon)$.[2]

---

[1] See, for example, Erwe I, Chapter II, 1.
[2] More briefly one says "if (20) holds for almost all n".

We shall now relate this definition to the above definition for the convergence of filters. Thus, let $\{a_n\}$ be a sequence of rational numbers which converges, in the sense of classical analysis, to a rational number a.[1] The sequence of remainders

$$r_n = \{a_{n+1}, a_{n+2}, a_{n+3}, \ldots\}, \qquad n = 1, 2, 3, \ldots$$

is, by VII 3, a filter $\mathfrak{R}$ of the rational topology. It converges to the number $a \in Q$ if it is a refinement of the neighbourhood filter $\mathfrak{U}(a)$. In Example (I) of VII 4 we defined this neighbourhood filter as the set of open intervals $]a-q, a+q[$. The convergence $\mathfrak{R} \to a$ (or $\lim \mathfrak{R} = a$) is thus established if, for every rational number $q > 0$, there exists at least one set r_n, that is contained in $]a-q, a+q[$: $r_n \in]a-q, a+q[$.

This can also be expressed as

$$|a_v - a| < q$$

for $v > n$. Hence (20) (with q instead of ε) is satisfied by our sequence; it is consequently convergent to a in the *classical sense*. Clearly the converse is also true. From $\lim a_n = a$ (in the sense of the theory of number sequences) follows the convergence of the remainder filter in the sense of the new definition.

The definition of convergence of filters also allows us to make statements in the rational topology about filters which do not have the character of number sequences. For instance, according to Example (I) of VII 4 we have for the filters $\mathfrak{U}_1(a)$ and $\mathfrak{U}_2(a)$

$$\lim \mathfrak{U}_1(a) = a, \qquad \lim \mathfrak{U}_2(a) = a$$

Let us next consider a few examples of other topological spaces.

(A). The filter $\mathfrak{F}_3$ (Example (III) of VII 3) converges to the origin of the plane.

(B). The set of open circular discs

$$x^2 + y^2 < 1 + \frac{1}{n}, \qquad n = 1, 2, 3, \ldots \tag{21}$$

forms a filter $\mathfrak{F}_B$ of the (x, y)-plane. This plane is a topological space in which distance is defined by (2) and the neighbourhood $\mathfrak{U}(x, y)$ of the point with coordinates x and y is the set of points with

---

[1] We limit ourselves to rational numbers since the real numbers will not be defined until later (Chapter VIII). The theorems and definitions concerning convergent sequences hold also for sequences of real numbers.

coordinates x_1 and y_1 for which

$$(x - x_1)^2 + (y - y_1)^2 < k$$

The neighbourhood filter $\mathfrak{U}(x, y)$ is thus a set of open and concentric circular discs. Clearly every point (x, y) possesses such neighbourhoods (with $k < 1$) which do not completely contain any of the circular discs (21). Hence the filter $\mathfrak{F}_B$ is not convergent.

(C). An examination of convergence in the space K_ρ of Example (G) of VII 3 brings to light some new aspects. In this case the neighbourhood of a point was given by a parallel strip, as shown in Fig. 34. The set of parallel strips for a fixed r then forms the neighbourhood filter $\mathfrak{U}(r)$ for *each* of the complex numbers $r + is$ (for arbitrary s). It converges to each of the numbers $r + is$ (for fixed r and arbitrary s).

It is possible for a filter to converge to different points a and b of a topological space T only if (as in our example) T is *not separable*.

In a separable topological space S a filter has at most one limit.
Assume that a filter $\mathfrak{F}$ has two limits a and b. Then

$$\mathfrak{F} \lhd \mathfrak{U}(a), \qquad \mathfrak{F} \lhd \mathfrak{U}(b), \qquad a \neq b \tag{22}$$

Now let $U(a)$ and $U(b)$ be two neighbourhoods of the points a and b whose intersection is empty

$$U(a) \cap U(b) = \varnothing \tag{23}$$

Since the space is separable, such neighbourhoods must exist. Then, by (22), for certain sets F_1 and F_2 of the filter we should have

$$U(a) \supset F_1 \in \mathfrak{F}, \qquad U(b) \supset F_2 \in \mathfrak{F}$$

By (23) it follows that

$$F_1 \cap F_2 \subset U(a) \cap U(b) = \varnothing$$

But by F3) and F2) the intersection of two sets of a filter cannot be empty. Hence the assumption (22) is false.

We note further the following theorem about the convergence of filters:

If $\mathfrak{F}_1 \lhd \mathfrak{F}_2$ and $\lim \mathfrak{F}_2 = a$, then $\lim \mathfrak{F}_1 = a$ also.

This follows directly from the transitive property (12) of the refinement relation.

6. ε-sets

The propositions[1] of paragraphs 6 and 7 of this chapter refer to the *rational topology*, i.e., to the set Q of rational numbers,[2] in which the neighbourhood of a point $r \in Q$ is given by the symmetric interval $]r - q, r + q[$.

A subset $M \subset Q$ is called an ε-set if, for all elements $r \in M$, $s \in M$, $|r - s| < ε$.

Consider a few examples.

(A). The open interval $]1, 2[$ is a 1-set (but also a 1·5 set, a 2-set, etc.).

(B). The set N of natural numbers is not an ε-set for any positive number ε.

(C). The sequence $\{0, 1, 0, 1, 0, 1, \ldots\}$ is an ε-set for all numbers $ε > 1$.

(D). The set $\{r\}$ ($r \in Q$) is an ε-set for *every* $ε > 0$.

For the subsets $A, B, C, \ldots$ of the rational topology we now define the operations $A + B$, $A - B$, and $A \cdot B$ as follows

$$A + B = \{a + b / a \in A \wedge b \in B\} \tag{24a}$$

$$A - B = \{a - b / a \in A \wedge b \in B\} \tag{24b}$$

$$A \cdot B = \{a \cdot b / a \in A \wedge b \in B\} \tag{24c}$$

We give a few examples.

(E). Let $A =]0, 1[$, $B =]1, 2[$. Then clearly

$$A + B =]1, 3[, \qquad A - B =]-2, 0[, \qquad A \cdot B =]0, 2[$$

(F). Let $A = \{r, s\}$, $B = \{s, t\}$. Then

$$A + B = \{r + s, r + t, 2s, s + t\}$$

$$A - B = \{r - s, r - t, 0, s - t\}$$

$$A \cdot B = \{r \cdot s, r \cdot t, s^2, s \cdot t\}$$

(G). Let $A = \{1\}$, $B = N$, the set of natural numbers. Then

$$A + B = \{2, 3, 4, \ldots\}, \qquad A - B = \{0, -1, -2, -3, \ldots\}$$

$$A \cdot B = N$$

[1] Some definitions and results can be carried over to other topological spaces. For example one can define calculations with sets for all topological spaces in which an addition (subtraction, multiplication) is defined for points of the space.

[2] The elements of Q are called *points* (of the topological space) or also (rational) numbers.

From the definitions (24) we have, for calculations with subsets of Q:

If $C \subset A$ and $D \subset B$, then

$$C + D \subset A + B, \qquad C - D \subset A - B, \qquad C \cdot D \subset A \cdot B$$

For subsets of Q that do not contain the number 0, we can also define the set M^{-1} as follows

$$M^{-1} = \frac{1}{M} = \left\{ x/x = \frac{1}{a} \wedge a \in M \right\} \tag{25}$$

Accordingly, for example, for the set N of natural numbers

$$\frac{1}{N} = \left\{ \frac{1}{n} \right\}, \qquad n = 1, 2, 3, \ldots$$

We shall now derive a few simple theorems for calculations with ε-sets.

If A is an ε-set and B is an η-set, then $A + B$ and $A - B$ are $(\varepsilon + \eta)$-sets.
We shall give the proof for $A - B$; the proof for $A + B$ is analogous.
Let $x \in A - B$, $y \in A - B$. Then $x = a - b$, $y = a' - b'$, where $a \in A$, $a' \in A$, $b \in B$, $b' \in B$.
For the difference $x - y$ we then have

$$|x - y| = |(a - b) - (a' - b')| = |(a - a') - (b - b')|$$
$$\leqslant |a - a'| + |b - b'| < \varepsilon + \eta$$

In preparation for the next theorem we note that *all ε-sets are bounded*. This means that there exists a rational number k, such that $|a| < k$ for all numbers a of an ε-set in Q.
For if a' is any (chosen and then fixed) number of the ε-set, then

$$|a| - |a'| \leqslant |a - a'|$$

so that

$$|a| < |a'| + \varepsilon = k$$

Now if A is an ε-set (with bound k_1) and B an η-set (with bound k_2), then there exists a common bound K for the absolute values of the elements of both sets A and B: $K = \text{Max}(k_1, k_2)$. We can now prove:

If the ε-set A and the η-set B have a common bound K, then $A \cdot B$ is a $K \cdot (\varepsilon + \eta)$-set.
For let $c = a \cdot b$, $c' = a' \cdot b'$, where $a \in A$, $a' \in A$, $b \in B$, $b' \in B$.

Then

$$|c - c'| = |ab - a'b'| = |(a - a')b + (b - b')a'|$$
$$\leqslant |a - a'| \cdot |b| + |b - b'| \cdot |a'| < K \cdot (\varepsilon + \eta)$$

For the set M^{-1} the following theorem holds:

If M is an ε-set of Q, with elements whose absolute values are bounded below

$$|a| > k, \qquad a \in M \tag{26}$$

then M^{-1} is an $\varepsilon \cdot k^{-2}$-set.

By (25) the elements of M^{-1} are of the form a^{-1} and b^{-1}, where $a \in M$, $b \in M$. For the difference of any two elements of M^{-1} we then have

$$\left| \frac{1}{a} - \frac{1}{b} \right| = \frac{|b - a|}{|a| \cdot |b|} < \frac{\varepsilon}{k^2}$$

7. Cauchy filters

In classical analysis a sequence of numbers $\{a_n\}$ is called a *Cauchy sequence* if for every $\varepsilon > 0$ there exists a number $N(\varepsilon)$ such that

$$|a_n - a_m| < \varepsilon \tag{27}$$

for $n > N(\varepsilon)$, $m > N(\varepsilon)$. Every convergent sequence is obviously a Cauchy sequence. On the other hand there are Cauchy sequences of rational numbers which do not converge to a rational number.[1]

By analogy with these Cauchy sequences we now define:

A filter $\mathfrak{F}$ on the rational topology is called a Cauchy filter if it contains ε-sets for every $\varepsilon > 0$.

Clearly the remainder filter associated with a Cauchy sequence is a Cauchy filter.[2] For the filter of the remainders is given by

$$\mathfrak{R} = \{r_n\} = \{\{a_{n+1}, a_{n+2}, a_{n+3}, \ldots\}\}, \qquad n = 1, 2, 3, \ldots$$

and, by (27), $\{r_n\}$ is an ε-set for sufficiently large n.

Further examples of C-filters are:

(I) the neighbourhood filter $\mathfrak{U}(a)$;
(II) the filters $\mathfrak{U}_1(a)$ and $\mathfrak{U}_2(a)$ defined in (I) of VII 4;

---

[1] See VIII 1.
[2] In the following this will usually be abbreviated to C-filter.

(III) the filter $\{\{q\}\}$, where $q \in Q$.

On the other hand, the set of intervals

$$\left\{\left]-\frac{1}{n}, 1+\frac{1}{n}\right[\right\} \qquad (n = 1, 2, 3, \ldots)$$

is a filter, but *not* a C-filter. Each element of this filter is an interval of length greater than 1.

From the definition of a C-filter we obtain at once:

(A). *If $\mathfrak{F}$ is a C-filter and $\mathfrak{G} \lhd \mathfrak{F}$, then $\mathfrak{G}$ is also a C-filter.*

From this it follows further that

(B). *Every convergent filter on Q is a C-filter.*

For it is a refinement of the neighbourhood filter, which we have already recognized as a C-filter.

For subsequent applications we must define the basic operations for filters. To do this we recall the general definitions of addition and multiplication of sets of rational numbers (p. 150). Since a filter is a set of sets of such numbers, we can also define addition and multiplication for filters on Q

$$\mathfrak{F} + \mathfrak{G} = \{F + G / F \in \mathfrak{F} \wedge G \in \mathfrak{G}\}$$
$$\mathfrak{F} \cdot \mathfrak{G} = \{F \cdot G / F \in \mathfrak{F} \wedge G \in \mathfrak{G}\} \tag{28}$$

We now show that $\mathfrak{F} + \mathfrak{G}$ and $\mathfrak{F} \cdot \mathfrak{G}$ are again filters. The justification of F1) and F2) is trivial. To show that F3) is satisfied we make use of the filter properties of $\mathfrak{F}$ and $\mathfrak{G}$. Accordingly, for any two sets F_1 and F_2 of the filter $\mathfrak{F}$ there exists a set $F_3 \in \mathfrak{F}$ which is contained in the intersection of the two sets. Thus we have

$$F_3 \subset F_1, \qquad F_3 \subset F_2 \tag{29a}$$

Similarly for $G_1 \in \mathfrak{G}$, $G_2 \in \mathfrak{G}$ there exists a set $G_3 \in \mathfrak{G}$ with the property

$$G_3 \subset G_1, \qquad G_3 \subset G_2 \tag{29b}$$

From the definition of addition of sets we have

$$(F_3 + G_3) \subset (F_1 + G_1), \qquad (F_3 + G_3) \subset (F_2 + G_2)$$

and hence also

$$(F_3 + G_3) \subset (F_1 + G_1) \cap (F_2 + G_2)$$

Thus $\mathfrak{F} + \mathfrak{G}$ is indeed a filter. The proof for $\mathfrak{F} \cdot \mathfrak{G}$ is on similar lines.

From the theorems about ε-sets established on p. 151 it now follows that:

(C). *The sum of two C-filters is a C-filter.*

(D). *The product of two C-filters is a C-filter.*

We shall confine ourselves to the proof of (D). Let F and G be sets of the filters $\mathfrak{F}$ and $\mathfrak{G}$ with the common bound k. Thus we have $F \in \mathfrak{F}$, $G \in \mathfrak{G}$ and $|f| < k$, $|g| < k$ for all elements $f \in F$ and $g \in G$. Now let F_1 and G_1 be $\varepsilon/2k$-sets of the filters $\mathfrak{F}$ and $\mathfrak{G}$. Such sets must exist, since $\mathfrak{F}$ and $\mathfrak{G}$ are C-filters. Then, by the filter property F3), there exist sets F_2 and G_2 with the properties

$$F_2 \in \mathfrak{F}, \qquad G_2 \in \mathfrak{G}, \qquad F_2 \subset F \cap F_1, \qquad G_2 \subset G \cap G_1$$

From $F_2 \subset F_1$, $G_2 \subset G_1$ it follows that both sets are also $\varepsilon/2k$-sets. The product of these two sets (see p. 151) is thus an ε-set. Hence we have shown that the filter $\mathfrak{F} \cdot \mathfrak{G}$ contains an ε-set; it is thus again a C-filter.

Now let $\mathfrak{F}$ be a C-filter of sets for which a positive lower bound exists.[1] Thus let

$$|f| > m \tag{30}$$

for all numbers $f \in F$, $F \in \mathfrak{F}$. *Then the set of sets defined by*

$$\mathfrak{F}^{-1} = \frac{1}{\mathfrak{F}} = \left\{ \frac{1}{F} \Big/ F \in \mathfrak{F} \right\} \tag{31}$$

is also a C-filter.

To prove this theorem we have to show that:

a) $\mathfrak{F}^{-1}$ is a filter;

b) $\mathfrak{F}^{-1}$ contains ε-sets for every $\varepsilon > 0$.

These proofs are left to the reader. To prove b) one uses the last theorem of VII 6.

We now define a new form of equivalence for C-filters.

Two filters $\mathfrak{C}_1$ and $\mathfrak{C}_2$ are called C-equivalent (written $\mathfrak{C}_1 \approx \mathfrak{C}_2$) if the union filter $\mathfrak{C}_1 \sqcup \mathfrak{C}_2$ is also a C-filter.

It is easy to see that C-equivalence has the usual equivalence properties. It is reflexive, symmetric, and transitive.

$$(\mathfrak{C}_1 \approx \mathfrak{C}_2 \Leftrightarrow \mathfrak{C}_2 \approx \mathfrak{C}_1) \tag{32a}$$

$$\mathfrak{C} \approx \mathfrak{C} \tag{32b}$$

$$(\mathfrak{C}_1 \approx \mathfrak{C}_2) \wedge (\mathfrak{C}_2 \approx \mathfrak{C}_3) \Rightarrow \mathfrak{C}_1 \approx \mathfrak{C}_3 \tag{32c}$$

[1] Such a filter is said to be *bounded below*.

(32a) and (32b) are trivial. To prove (32c) we begin with $\varepsilon/2$-sets $C_1 \cup C_2$ and $C_2 \cup C_3$ of the C-filters $\mathfrak{C}_1 \sqcup \mathfrak{C}_2$ and $\mathfrak{C}_2 \sqcup \mathfrak{C}_3$. Since the intersection of these two sets is not empty

$$(C_1 \cup C_2) \cup (C_2 \cup C_3) = C_1 \cup C_2 \cup C_3$$

is an ε-set. Hence $C_1 \cup C_3 \in \mathfrak{C}_1 \sqcup \mathfrak{C}_3$ is, *a fortiori*, an ε-set. But this means that $\mathfrak{C}_1 \sqcup \mathfrak{C}_3$ is a C-filter, and we have in fact $\mathfrak{C}_1 \approx \mathfrak{C}_3$.

Two C-filters which converge to the same number $q \in Q$ are C-equivalent.

To prove this basic theorem we begin with the definition of convergence. If the C-filters $\mathfrak{C}_1$ and $\mathfrak{C}_2$ converge to $q \in Q$, then

$$\mathfrak{C}_1 \lhd \mathfrak{U}(q), \qquad \mathfrak{C}_2 \lhd \mathfrak{U}(q) \tag{33},$$

Let $U(q)$ be an arbitrary neighbourhood of q. Then by (33) there exist sets $C_1 \in \mathfrak{C}_1$ and $C_2 \in \mathfrak{C}_2$ that are contained in $U(q)$

$$C_1 \subset U(q), \qquad C_2 \subset U(q)$$

But from this it follows that the union of C_1 and C_2 also belongs to $U(q)$: $C_1 \cup C_2 \subset U(q)$. Thus $\mathfrak{C}_1 \sqcup \mathfrak{C}_2 \lhd \mathfrak{U}(q)$, and this completes the proof.

We must now relate the newly defined C-equivalence ($\approx$) to the 'ordinary' equivalence ($\sim$) which we introduced earlier for arbitrary filters. We shall prove that:

C-equivalence is 'coarser' than ordinary equivalence. More explicitly this means:

From $\mathfrak{C}_1 \sim \mathfrak{C}_2$ it always follows that $\mathfrak{C}_1 \approx \mathfrak{C}_2$, but not conversely. We first prove

$$\mathfrak{C}_1 \sim \mathfrak{C}_2 \Rightarrow \mathfrak{C}_1 \approx \mathfrak{C}_2 \tag{34}$$

Let $\mathfrak{C}_1$ and $\mathfrak{C}_2$ be equivalent filters

$$\mathfrak{C}_1 \sim \mathfrak{C}_2 \tag{35}$$

By (35) we have, among other things, $\mathfrak{C}_1 \lhd \mathfrak{C}_2$. Hence for each $C_2 \in \mathfrak{C}_2$ there exists a $C_1 \in \mathfrak{C}_1$ with $C_1 \subset C_2$. But, since $C_2 \subset C_2$, we also have $(C_1 \cup C_2) \subset C_2$. Thus

$$\mathfrak{C}_1 \sqcup \mathfrak{C}_2 \lhd \mathfrak{C}_2$$

Since $\mathfrak{C}_2$ is a C-filter, $\mathfrak{C}_1 \sqcup \mathfrak{C}_2$ is also one, and consequently $\mathfrak{C}_1 \approx \mathfrak{C}_2$.

In order to show that (34) is not, in general, reversible, we need only give an example of two C-filters, which are C-equivalent but not equivalent in the sense of the definition of VII 4.

We can take, for example, the remainder filter of a sequence of numbers which converges to a number $a \in Q$, together with another filter which converges to a, and whose elements are intervals. For instance (for $a = 0$)

$$\mathfrak{C}_1 = \left\{\left\{\frac{1}{n+1}, \frac{1}{n+2}, \frac{1}{n+3}, \ldots\right\}\right\}, \qquad \mathfrak{C}_2 = \left\{\left]-\frac{1}{n}, +\frac{1}{n}\right[\right\}$$

$$n = 1, 2, 3, \ldots$$

Clearly $\mathfrak{C}_1 \sqcup \mathfrak{C}_2$ is also a C-filter. Hence we have $\mathfrak{C}_1 \approx \mathfrak{C}_2$. Moreover $\mathfrak{C}_1 \lhd \mathfrak{C}_2$, but *not* $\mathfrak{C}_2 \lhd \mathfrak{C}_1$. Hence $\mathfrak{C}_1$ and $\mathfrak{C}_2$ are not equivalent.

8. Problems

1. Show that the set of sequences $\{x_1, x_2, x_3, \ldots\}$ $(x_k \in Q)$ forms a metric space in which distance is given by

$$D(x, y) = \sum_{n=1}^{\infty} \frac{|x_n - y_n|}{n^2(1 + |x_n - y_n|)}$$

2. Prove that the remainders of the sequence $\{0, 1, 0, 1, 0, 1, \ldots\}$ form a filter on Q. Show that it is not convergent.
3. Give a definition for the convergence of an infinite series using the filter concept.
4. Which of the following sets of sets are filters? Which are C-filters on Q?

(a) $\left\{\left\{\left(1+\frac{1}{n}\right)^n, \left(1+\frac{1}{n+1}\right)^{n+1}, \ldots\right\}\right\}, \qquad n = 1, 2, 3, \ldots$

(b) $\{]3-n, 3+n[\}, \qquad n = 1, 2, 3, \ldots$

(c) $\{]n, n+1[\}, \qquad n = 1, 2, 3, \ldots$

(d) $\{\{P(x, y)/2x^2 + y^2 < 1 + k \wedge k > 0\}\}$

(e) $\left\{\left]-\frac{1}{n}, +\frac{1}{n}\right[\cup \left]1-\frac{1}{m}, 1+\frac{1}{m}\right[\right\},$

$$n = 1, 2, 3, \ldots, \qquad m = 1, 2, 3, \ldots$$

5. Which of the filters 4(a) to 4(e) converges to a number $q \in Q$?

6. What refinement relations exist between the filters

$$\mathfrak{F}_1 = \left\{\left]-\frac{1}{n^2}, +\frac{1}{n^2}\right[\right\}, \qquad \mathfrak{F}_2 = \left\{\left]-\frac{1}{n}, \frac{1}{n+2}\right[\right\},$$

$$\mathfrak{F}_3 = \left\{\frac{n^2}{n!}, \frac{(n+1)^2}{(n+1)!}, \cdots\right\}, \qquad n = 1, 2, 3, \ldots.$$

7. Which of the filters mentioned in 6 are equivalent, and which are C-equivalent?

CHAPTER EIGHT

Real Numbers

1. Completeness

We have shown in Chapter VII that all filters of the rational topology that converge to a number $q \in Q$ are C-filters. The converse of this statement does not hold. There are C-filters on Q which do not converge to a number $q \in Q$.

As an example consider the remainder filter of the sequence

$$\{e_n\} = \left\{1 + \frac{1}{1!} + \frac{1}{2!} + \ldots + \frac{1}{n!}\right\}, \qquad n = 1, 2, 3, \ldots \qquad (1)$$

Clearly

$$\mathfrak{F} = \{\{e_{n+1}, e_{n+2}, e_{n+3}, \ldots\}\}, \qquad n = 1, 2, 3, \ldots \qquad (2)$$

is a C-filter, since for $M > N$

$$e_M - e_N = \frac{1}{(N+1)!} + \frac{1}{(N+2)!} + \ldots + \frac{1}{M!}$$

$$\leqslant \frac{1}{(N+1)!}\left(1 + \frac{1}{N+2} + \ldots + \frac{1}{(N+2)^{M-N-1}}\right)$$

But

$$1 + q + q^2 + \ldots + q^r = \frac{1 - q^{r+1}}{1 - q} < \frac{1}{1 - q}$$

for $0 < q < 1$, and consequently, for $M > N \geqslant n > 1$

$$|e_M - e_N| = e_M - e_N < \frac{N+2}{(N+1)! \cdot (N+1)} < \frac{2}{(N+1)!} \leqslant \frac{2}{(n+1)!} \qquad (2')$$

Hence the filter (2) contains ε-sets for every $\varepsilon > 0$. Nevertheless there exists no number $q \in Q$ to which it converges. For suppose that

$$\lim \mathfrak{F} = q = \frac{a}{b} \tag{3}$$

where the natural numbers a and b are relatively prime.[1]

As we know, in filter theory convergence is defined for filters of other types. But in the case of *remainder filters* one can regard the filter-theoretical statement (3) and the classical formula (3′) as synonymous.

(3) implies that $\mathfrak{F}$ is a refinement of the neighbourhood filter $\mathfrak{U}(q)$. In particular, for sufficiently large n we should have[2]

$$d = \frac{a}{b} - \left(1 + \frac{1}{1!} + \frac{1}{2!} + \ldots + \frac{1}{n!}\right) < \frac{1}{5b!} \tag{4}$$

Then, for $n > b$

$$\left[\frac{a \cdot b!}{b} - \left(2b! + \frac{b!}{2!} + \ldots + \frac{b!}{b!}\right)\right] - \left[\frac{b!}{(b+1)!} + \ldots + \frac{b!}{n!}\right] < \frac{1}{5} \tag{5}$$

The number in the first bracket of (5) is an integer g. Since

$$\frac{1}{b+1}\left[1 + \frac{1}{b+2} + \frac{1}{(b+2)(b+3)} + \ldots + \frac{1}{(b+2)(b+3)\ldots n}\right]$$

$$\leq \frac{1}{b+1} \sum_{v=0}^{n} \frac{1}{(b+2)^v} < \frac{1}{b+1} \cdot \frac{1}{1 - \dfrac{1}{b+2}} = \frac{b+2}{(b+1)^2}$$

it follows from (5) that

$$g - \frac{b+2}{(b+1)^2} < \frac{1}{5} \tag{6}$$

But, as can easily be shown

$$\left\{ \frac{b+2}{(b+1)^2} \qquad (b = 1, 2, 3, \ldots) \right.$$

<hr>

[1] In classical analysis the limit is made to correspond, not to the remainder filter (*e.g.* (2)), but to the sequence itself (here (1)). Instead of (3) one writes

$$q = \frac{a}{b} = \lim_{n \to \infty} e_n \tag{3′}$$

[2] The reader should justify the omission of the modulus sign in (4).

is a monotonic decreasing sequence. Hence

$$\frac{b+2}{(b+1)^2} \leqslant \frac{1+2}{(1+1)^2} = \frac{3}{4}$$

and it follows from (6) that

$$\tfrac{1}{4} = 1 - \tfrac{3}{4} \leqslant g - \tfrac{3}{4} < \tfrac{1}{5}$$

This is false, and hence the assumption (3) must be incorrect.

It is not difficult to find other examples of C-filters on Q, which do not converge to a number $q \in Q$. One only has to begin with any sequence $\{a_n\}$ $(n = 1, 2, 3, \ldots)$ for which the remainder filter *of the squares* converges to 2.[1] Thus let

$$\mathfrak{F}^{(2)} = \{\{a_{n+1}^2, a_{n+2}^2, a_{n+3}^2, \ldots\}\} \qquad (n = 1, 2, 3, \ldots)$$

be a filter for which[2]

$$\lim \mathfrak{F}^{(2)} = 2 \qquad (7)$$

One can obtain such a sequence $\{a_n\}$, for example, as a sequence of decimal fractions

$$a_n = 1 \cdot b_1 b_2 b_3 \ldots b_n \qquad (n = 1, 2, 3, \ldots)$$

for which

$$(1 \cdot b_1 b_2 \ldots b_n)^2 < 2, \qquad (1 \cdot b_1 b_2 \ldots b_{n-1}(b_n+1))^2 > 2$$

for all numbers n. Clearly

$$1 \cdot 4; \ 1 \cdot 41; \ 1 \cdot 414; \ 1 \cdot 4142; \ldots \qquad (8)$$

are the first numbers of this sequence.

It is easy to see that the set of sets

$$\{\{a_{n+1}, a_{n+2}, a_{n+3}, \ldots\}\} \qquad (n = 1, 2, 3, \ldots) \qquad (9)$$

is then also a C-filter. If it were to converge to a rational number q, then obviously $q^2 = 2$. But it is known that[3] no rational number exists which has a square equal to 2. Thus (9) is a C-filter for which *no limit exists* in the space Q.

[1] Instead of 2 one can take any other natural number that is not a perfect square.

[2] In the language of classical analysis one writes
$$\lim a_n^2 = 2 \qquad (7')$$

[3] See, for example, Meschkowski (2), p. 9, et seq.

The results of our considerations can be made clearer by two schematic representations. The C-filters that converge to a number $q \in Q$ are pairwise equivalent, and each filter which is C-equivalent to such a filter also converges to q. We denote the class[1] of filters that converge to the rational number q by $\alpha(q)$ and represent them symbolically by arrows which are directed towards q, as shown in Fig. 40a.

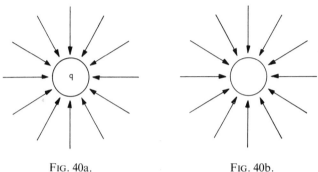

FIG. 40a.   FIG. 40b.

Now let β be the class of filters that are C-equivalent to (9). If this class is also represented by a set of arrows, then we have to leave the space in the middle empty, (Fig. 40b), since there is no rational number towards which the filter converges.

It is desirable to fill in the hole of Fig. 40b. To do this we must obviously extend the set Q of rational numbers to a new set of 'numbers', which contains Q as a proper subset. Moreover we want to be able to interpret this set also as a topological space.

One must not over-simplify this task. It is not permissible to reason thus: "No rational number exists which has a square equal to 2; hence this shows that $\sqrt{2}$ is an *irrational* number." We have only shown that, among the numbers known so far, none exists whose square is 2. If one finds this state of affairs disturbing,[2] then one must first of all *create* new numbers by a meaningful definition. This 'act of creation' is not entirely simple. The definition must be such that calculations (addition, multiplication, etc.) can be performed with the newly defined 'objects'. The already known rational numbers must turn out to be subsets of the newly defined set of the

---

[1] *Class* is used as a synonym for *set*.

[2] In Greek mathematics one was satisfied with the observation that the side and the diagonal of a square are *incommensurable* (see, for example, Meschkowski (2), p. 9, et seq.). But this suggests the desirability of having a *number* as a measure of the length of the diagonal of the unit square.

real numbers, and finally this set must be a field with the same rules for calculation that are valid for Q. Only when this has been achieved, is one justified in working with 'numbers' $\sqrt{2}$, $\sqrt{3}$, etc.

It has been customary to give this definition by means of nests of intervals or Dedekind sections.[1] The use of the filter concept, which has proved so fruitful in general topology, suggests itself today.

Definition. A class of C-equivalent C-filters is called a real number. In the following we shall denote these real numbers by small Greek letters, or also in the form $\alpha = [\mathfrak{C}]$, where $\mathfrak{C}$ is any filter of the class α. Thus the real numbers are sets of filters, *i.e.*, sets of sets of sets. They are characterized by *any one* of the filters belonging to the class α.

We shall illustrate this by some examples.
Let

$$\mathfrak{F}_1 = \left\{ \left] 1 - \frac{1}{n}, 1 + \frac{1}{n} \right[\right\}, \qquad (n = 1, 2, 3, \ldots)$$

$$\mathfrak{F}_2 = \left\{ \left\{ \sqrt[n+1]{n+1}, \sqrt[n+2]{n+2}, \ldots \right\} \right\}, \qquad (n = 1, 2, 3, \ldots)$$

Clearly

$$\mathfrak{F}_1 \approx \mathfrak{F}_2, \qquad \lim \mathfrak{F}_1 = \lim \mathfrak{F}_2 = 1$$

If we denote the set of filters that are C-equivalent to $\mathfrak{F}_1$ or $\mathfrak{F}_2$ by α, then we have[2]

$$\alpha = [\mathfrak{F}_1] = [\mathfrak{F}_2] = [\{\{1\}\}] \qquad (10)$$

By Example VIII, 1 the remainder filter defined by (2) of the sequence (1) is C-equivalent to the remainder filter $\mathfrak{G}$ of the sequence

$$\{e^{(n)}\} = \left\{ \left(1 + \frac{1}{n} \right)^n \right\}, \qquad n = 1, 2, 3, \ldots$$

These two remainder filters thus determine the same class of C-equivalent C-filters, and hence the same real number[3] ε

$$\varepsilon = [\mathfrak{F}] = [\mathfrak{G}]$$

[1] See, for example, Feigl-Rohrbach, Lenz, or Vogel.
[2] For the meaning of $\{\{1\}\}$ see Example (VII) in VII 3. Later we shall simply write
$$\alpha = [\{\{1\}\}] = 1$$
[3] In general this real number is denoted by e: $e = 2 \cdot 718281828 \ldots$.

We shall now show that the given definition of real numbers is meaningful by proving the following theorems:

(I). *The set R of real numbers is an 'extension field' of the set Q of rational numbers.*

(II). *R can be interpreted (with a suitable definition of the 'neighbourhood' of a point) as a separable topological space.*

(III). *Every C-filter on R has a limit in R.*

A topological space with C-filters is said to be *complete* if every C-filter defined in this space possesses a limit which *belongs to the space.* According to our results, *the rational topology is not complete.* By the statement (III), however, the space R of real numbers *is* complete.

2. Calculations with real numbers

Let $\alpha = [\mathfrak{C}]$ and $\beta = [\mathfrak{D}]$ be real numbers. The sum $\alpha + \beta$ and the product $\alpha . \beta$ are defined by

$$\alpha + \beta = [\mathfrak{C} + \mathfrak{D}] \tag{11}$$

$$\alpha . \beta = [\mathfrak{C} . \mathfrak{D}] \tag{12}$$

By the theorem proved on p. 154, $\mathfrak{C} + \mathfrak{D}$ and $\mathfrak{C} . \mathfrak{D}$ are again C-filters. We now have to show that the definitions given by (11) and (12) are *independent of the particular choice of the 'representative' filters $\mathfrak{C}$ and $\mathfrak{D}$.* More explicitly we have to show that, from

$$\mathfrak{C}_1 \approx \mathfrak{C}_2, \qquad \mathfrak{D}_1 \approx \mathfrak{D}_2 \ (\mathfrak{C}_1, \mathfrak{C}_2 \in \alpha; \ \mathfrak{D}_1, \mathfrak{D}_2 \in \beta) \tag{13}$$

follow

$$\mathfrak{C}_1 + \mathfrak{D}_1 \approx \mathfrak{C}_2 + \mathfrak{D}_2 \tag{14}$$

and

$$\mathfrak{C}_1 . \mathfrak{D}_1 \approx \mathfrak{C}_2 . \mathfrak{D}_2 \tag{15}$$

We shall confine ourselves to the proof of (15). The simpler proof of (14) is left to the reader.

Let $C_\nu, D_\nu \ (\nu = 1, 2)$ be arbitrary bounded sets of the filters $\mathfrak{C}_\nu, \mathfrak{D}_\nu$ respectively. Let K be a common bound for the four sets. We note from (13) that the two union filters $\mathfrak{C}_1 \sqcup \mathfrak{C}_2$ and $\mathfrak{D}_1 \sqcup \mathfrak{D}_2$ are C-filters. Then, for any arbitrarily chosen positive number ε, there exist $(2K)^{-1} . \varepsilon$-sets of these filters

$$F' = C'_1 \cup C'_2 \in \mathfrak{F} = \mathfrak{C}_1 \sqcup \mathfrak{C}_2, \qquad G' = D'_1 \cup D'_2 \in \mathfrak{G} = \mathfrak{D}_1 \sqcup \mathfrak{D}_2$$

But $F = C_1 \cup C_2$, $G = D_1 \cup D_2$ are also elements of $\mathfrak{F}$, $\mathfrak{G}$ respectively. By the third filter axiom, therefore, there exist elements $F'' \subset F \cap F'$, $G'' \subset G \cap G'$ which also belong to $\mathfrak{F}$, $\mathfrak{G}$ respectively. Let

$$F'' = C_1'' \cup C_2'', \qquad G'' = D_1'' \cup D_2''$$

These two sets (as subsets of F and F', G and G' respectively) are $(2K)^{-1} \cdot \varepsilon$-sets; for both, K is a bound.

Now let c_v, d_v ($v = 1, 2$) be arbitrary elements of C'', D'' respectively. Then

$$|c_1 d_1 - c_2 d_2| = |c_1(d_1 - d_2) + d_2(c_1 - c_2)| < \frac{2 \cdot K \cdot \varepsilon}{2K} = \varepsilon \quad (16)$$

On the other hand (by the theorem of VII 6 on products of ε-sets) the sets $C_1'' \cdot D_1''$ and $C_2'' \cdot D_2''$ are ε-sets. Hence it follows from (16) that $C_1'' D_1'' \cup C_2'' D_2''$ is an ε-set. Thus $\mathfrak{C}_1 \mathfrak{D}_1 \sqcup \mathfrak{C}_2 \mathfrak{D}_2$ is a C-filter and (15) is proved.

The result just derived can be interpreted as follows. The real numbers

$$\alpha = [\mathfrak{C}] = [\mathfrak{C}'], \qquad \beta = [\mathfrak{D}] = [\mathfrak{D}'] \quad (17)$$

can be represented by *each* of their filters $\mathfrak{C}$, $\mathfrak{C}'$, etc., $\mathfrak{D}$, $\mathfrak{D}'$, etc. In the formation of products (or sums) it is immaterial which of the 'representatives' is put into the square bracket. For example, from (17) we have for the product $\alpha \cdot \beta$

$$\alpha \cdot \beta = [\mathfrak{C} \cdot \mathfrak{D}] = [\mathfrak{C}' \cdot \mathfrak{D}'] = [\mathfrak{C}' \cdot \mathfrak{D}] = [\mathfrak{C} \cdot \mathfrak{D}']$$

For the representation of a real number by a representative filter one will obviously choose a particularly simple one. This is always possible for those classes of filters which converge to a rational number. For example, let $\alpha(1)$ be the class of C-filters that converge to 1. The simplest filter of this class is clearly $[\{\{1\}\}]$, and hence one can write the real number $\alpha(1)$ as

$$\alpha(1) = [\{\{1\}\}] = \bar{1}$$

We shall introduce the bar as an abbreviation for those classes of C-equivalent C-filters that converge to a rational number q. Thus we write $\bar{q}$ as an abbreviation for $[\{\{q\}\}]$.

Hence the real number $\bar{0}$ is given by $[\{\{0\}\}]$, *i.e.*, by the set of C-filters that converge to the rational number 0. By our definition of real numbers it is clear that (for $\alpha = [\mathfrak{C}]$)

$$\alpha + \bar{0} = [\mathfrak{C} + \{\{0\}\}] = [\mathfrak{C}] = \alpha \qquad (18)$$

for all real numbers α.

We shall now show that the set R of real numbers forms a *field* with respect to the addition and multiplication defined above. According to V 1 we must first convince ourselves that the 5 *ring axioms* are satisfied. We then have to show further that the ring is commutative and that division by non-zero numbers is possible.

The validity of $\boldsymbol{R}_1$, $\boldsymbol{R}_2$, $\boldsymbol{R}_4$, $\boldsymbol{R}_5$ and that of the commutative law of multiplication

$$\alpha \cdot \beta = \beta \cdot \alpha \qquad (19)$$

follow at once from the fact that the corresponding laws hold for the rational numbers. From the definitions for calculations with sets, these laws can be carried over at once to the addition and multiplication of sets, and finally to calculations with filters, which are sets of sets.

The proof that $\boldsymbol{R}_3$ applies also to real numbers is rather more difficult.

For any two real numbers α and β there exists exactly one number ξ that satisfies the equation

$$\alpha + \xi = \beta \qquad (20)$$

To prove this theorem we first give the definition of the number $-\alpha = -[\mathfrak{C}]$

$$-\alpha = [\{\{-1\}\}] \cdot [\mathfrak{C}] = [\{\{-1\}\} \cdot \mathfrak{C}]$$

Recalling the definition of multiplication of sets (VII 6), we see at once that the change from α to $-\alpha$ is performed by replacing in every set of the filter every rational number a by $-a$.

To prove the theorem that subtraction is possible for real numbers, we first show: *for all real numbers*

$$\alpha + (-\alpha) = \bar{0} \qquad (21)$$

If $\alpha = [\mathfrak{C}]$, then (21) can also be written in the form

$$[\mathfrak{C}] + [-\mathfrak{C}] = [\mathfrak{C} - \mathfrak{C}] = [\mathfrak{C} + \{\{-1\}\} \cdot \mathfrak{C}] = \bar{0} \qquad (21')$$

To prove (21) we begin with an arbitrary ε-set C of the filter $\mathfrak{C}$. Then also the set $C + (-C)$ belongs to the filter $\mathfrak{C} + \{\{-1\}\} \cdot \mathfrak{C}$. The elements of this set can be written in the form

$$c_1 + (-c_2) = c_1 - c_2 \qquad (c_\nu \in C, \nu = 1, 2)$$

Since C is an ε-set, $|c_1 - c_2| < \varepsilon$. Thus $C + (-C)$ is an ε-set to which the number 0 ($0 = c_1 - c_2$) belongs as an element. Consequently $\mathfrak{C} + \{\{-1\}\}$. $\mathfrak{C}$ converges to 0, and (21) is proved.

We can now show that the subtraction problem (20) is uniquely soluble. Let $\alpha = [\mathfrak{C}]$, $\beta = [\mathfrak{D}]$. Then (20) assumes the form

$$[\mathfrak{C}] + \xi = [\mathfrak{D}] \tag{20'}$$

This equation is clearly satisfied by

$$\xi = [\mathfrak{D}] + [\{\{-1\}\} . \mathfrak{C}] \tag{22}$$

We have, in fact (noting the rules for calculations with real numbers),

$$[\mathfrak{C}] + ([\mathfrak{D}] + [\{\{-1\}\}\mathfrak{C}]) = [\mathfrak{D}] + [\mathfrak{C} + \{\{-1\}\}\mathfrak{C}]$$
$$= [\mathfrak{D}] + \bar{0} = [\mathfrak{D}]$$

Hence (22) is a solution of the equation (20'), and one can easily see[1] that this is the only solution of the 'subtraction problem'. Hence we have shown:

The set R of real numbers forms a commutative ring.

In a similar manner one can show that the equation

$$[\mathfrak{C}] . \xi = [\mathfrak{D}]$$

for the case $[\mathfrak{C}] \neq \bar{0}$ has the unique solution

$$\xi = [\mathfrak{D}] . \left[\frac{1}{\mathfrak{C}}\right]$$

The details of this proof are left to the reader. We thus arrive at the final result:

The set R of the real numbers is a field with respect to the operations defined above.

In IV 4 we introduced the concept of *isomorphism* for groups. Obviously this can easily be extended to other algebraic structures, e.g., to fields. Two fields K and K^* are said to be *isomorphic* if there is a one-to-one correspondence $k \leftrightarrow k^*$ between the elements $k \in K$ and $k^* \in K^*$ which is preserved under the field operations. Thus for $a, b \in K$, $a^*, b^* \in K^*$

$$(a+b)^* = a^* + b^*, \qquad (ab)^* = a^* . b^* \tag{23}$$

---

[1] One adds $[\{\{-1\}\} . \mathfrak{C}]$ to both sides of equation (20').

The field R of real numbers contains as a subset a field $\bar{Q}$ which is isomorphic to the field Q of rational numbers. The elements of this 'subfield' $\bar{Q}$ of R are the real numbers $\bar{q} = [\{\{q\}\}]$ corresponding to the rational numbers $q \in Q$. Clearly the laws corresponding to (23) hold, viz.

$$[\{\{q\}\}] + [\{\{r\}\}] = [\{\{q+r\}\}]$$
$$[\{\{q\}\}] \cdot [\{\{r\}\}] = [\{\{q \cdot r\}\}]$$

(24)

According to the definitions given so far we must distinguish carefully between the rational number q and the corresponding real number $\bar{q}$. q is a (rational) number, $\bar{q}$ a class of filters, i.e. a class of sets of sets. Each filter from $\bar{q}$ converges to the rational number q. For ease of expression one often *identifies* the field Q with the isomorphic field $\bar{Q}$. One then says: The field Q of rational numbers is a subfield of the field R of real numbers; every rational number is also a real number.

For subsequent applications we shall prove the following auxiliary theorem.

If a C-filter $\mathfrak{C}$ does not converge to 0, then there exists a C-filter $\mathfrak{C}'$ which is bounded above and below and is equivalent to $\mathfrak{C}$.

To prove this we begin with the fact that there exists a certain neighbourhood $]-q, +q[$ of 0 in which no set of $\mathfrak{C}$ is *entirely* contained; otherwise we should have $\mathfrak{C} \lhd \mathfrak{U}(0)$. Hence in every set $C \in \mathfrak{C}$ there is an element x with $|x| \geqslant q$. In particular let C be a $\frac{q}{2}$-set of $\mathfrak{C}$. Then, by definition, we have for all elements $c \in C$

$$|c - x| < \frac{q}{2}$$

Since $|x| \geqslant q$ it follows that $|c| > \frac{q}{2}$. Thus C has the lower bound $\frac{q}{2}$. As a $\frac{q}{2}$-set, C is, of course, also bounded above. The set of sets defined by

$$\mathfrak{C}' = \{C'/C' \subset C \wedge C' \in \mathfrak{C}\}$$

is clearly a C-filter. It is equivalent to $\mathfrak{C}$ and thus, *a fortiori*, C-equivalent. For we have, for every $C' \in \mathfrak{C}'$,

$$C' \subset C', \qquad C' \in \mathfrak{C}', \qquad C' \in \mathfrak{C}$$

It follows from this that

$$\mathfrak{C} \lhd \mathfrak{C}', \qquad \mathfrak{C}' \lhd \mathfrak{C},$$

and hence

$$\mathfrak{C} \sim \mathfrak{C}'$$

3. Ordering of the real numbers

To order real numbers we first define the concept of the *positive real number.*

A real number α is said to be positive, if there exists a C-filter $\mathfrak{C} \in \alpha$ *which is bounded below,*[1] *and whose sets consist of positive rational numbers.*

For example, the real number defined by

$$\varepsilon = \left[\left\{\left\{\left(1+\frac{1}{n}\right)^n, \left(1+\frac{1}{n+1}\right)^{n+1}, \ldots\right\}\right\}\right] \tag{25}$$

is positive: for all rational numbers of the form $\left(1+\frac{1}{n}\right)^n$ are greater than 1.

The set R^+ of the positive real numbers has the following properties:

(A). $\bar{0} \notin R^+$;

(B). If $\alpha \in R^+$ and $\beta \in R^+$, then also $\alpha + \beta \in R^+$, $\alpha \cdot \beta \in R^+$;

(C). If $\alpha \neq \bar{0}$, then either α or $(-\alpha)$ is positive.

The very simple proofs of (A) and (B) are left to the reader, and we shall confine ourselves to the proof of (C).

Since $\alpha \neq \bar{0}$, there exists a filter $\mathfrak{C} \in \alpha$ which is bounded below.[2] Let $q > 0$, say, be a rational lower bound for $\mathfrak{C}$. Then the interval $]-q, +q[$ is free of sets from $\mathfrak{C}$. Since $\mathfrak{C}$ is a C-filter, it must also contain q-sets. Every q-set of $\mathfrak{C}$ then consists entirely of positive or entirely of negative rational numbers. Let N^*, for example, be such a q-set, which consists entirely of *negative* rational numbers. Then the set of sets

$$\mathfrak{C}' = \{C'/C' \subset N^* \wedge C' \in \mathfrak{C}\}$$

is clearly a C-filter which is equivalent to $\mathfrak{C}$. We can then write α

[1] See the definition in VII 7.

[2] See the auxiliary theorem at the end of VIII 2.

in the form $\alpha = [\mathfrak{C}']$ and we have thus proved that $(-\alpha)$ is *positive*. If, instead, there exists in the filter $\mathfrak{C} \in \alpha$ a q-set P^* consisting of only positive numbers, then α itself is positive.

It cannot occur that α and $(-\alpha)$ are *both* positive. For, in that case, by (B) we should also have $\alpha + (-\alpha) = \bar{0}$ positive, which would contradict (A).

With these preparations we can now define an ordering for the set R of real numbers.

Let α and β be real numbers. Then $\alpha < \beta$ if $\beta - \alpha \in R^+$:

$$\alpha < \beta \Leftrightarrow \beta - \alpha \in R^+ \tag{26}$$

This ordering relation defined by (26) has the following properties:[1]

  (a) It is antireflexive (in the sense of II 7);
  (b) $[\alpha > \beta > \bar{0} \wedge \gamma \in R^+] \Rightarrow [\alpha + \gamma > \beta + \gamma]$;
  (c) $[\alpha > \beta > \bar{0} \wedge \gamma \in R^+] \Rightarrow \alpha.\gamma > \beta.\gamma$;
  (d) $[\alpha > \beta \wedge \alpha.\beta \in R^+] \Rightarrow \dfrac{1}{\beta} > \dfrac{1}{\alpha}$.

The proof of properties (a) to (d) is very simple and may be left to the reader.

The ordering defined here is naturally also applicable to the elements of the subset $\bar{Q} \subset R$. It can be shown that the ordering of the elements $\bar{q} \in \bar{Q}$ corresponds exactly to the ordering of the rational numbers $q \in Q$. We have (for $r \in Q$, $s \in Q$):

$$(r > s) \Leftrightarrow (\bar{r} > \bar{s}) \tag{27}$$

To see this we have only to define the number $\bar{r} - \bar{s}$ by the filter $\{\{r - s\}\}$:

$$\bar{r} - \bar{s} = \overline{r - s} = [\{\{r - s\}\}].$$

If $r > s$, then the filter $\{\{r - s\}\}$ is certainly bounded below, so that $\bar{r} > \bar{s}$. Since the argument is reversible, we have established (27).

Finally we note the following theorem about the ordering in R:

The ordering of the real numbers is archimedean. More precisely this means:[2] For two positive numbers α and β there always exists a natural number n, such that

$$\bar{n}.\alpha > \beta \tag{28}$$

---

[1] $\alpha > \beta$ stands for $\beta < \alpha$.
[2] Cf. problems III, 7 and 8.

Since $\alpha > \bar{0}$, this inequality (28) is satisfied if, and only if,

$$\bar{n} > \frac{\beta}{\alpha} = \gamma \qquad (28')$$

We thus have to show that *for every positive real number γ, there exists a natural number n for which $\bar{n} > \gamma$.*

Let $\mathfrak{C}$ be a filter belonging to γ which is bounded above and below. Such a filter must exist, by the auxiliary theorem of VIII 2. Let the rational number K be an upper bound for $\mathfrak{C}$, $n > K$. Then the sets of C-filters $\{\{n\}\} - \mathfrak{C}$ are bounded below by $n - K \in Q^{+}$.[1] Therefore $[\{\{n\}\} - \mathfrak{C}] = \bar{n} - \gamma \in R^{+}$, and hence $\bar{n} > \gamma$.

4. The topology in *R*

By the definition of an ordering relation in R we are in a position to define intervals $]\alpha, \beta[$ for real numbers α and β:

$$]\alpha, \beta[\; = \; \{\gamma/\gamma \in R \wedge \alpha < \gamma < \beta\} \qquad (29)$$

This enables us to introduce an 'interval topology' in R. Let α be an arbitrary element of R. Then every interval[2]

$$]\alpha - \bar{q}, \alpha + \bar{q}[\qquad (q \in Q)$$

is called a *neighbourhood* of α; the set of these intervals is the neighbourhood filter $\mathfrak{U}(\alpha)$. It is easy to see that the neighbourhood thus defined has all the properties required in Chapter VI. By this definition R becomes a *topological space*. It is also called the *real topology*.

The real topology is separable.

The proof is similar to that for the rational topology.

We introduced real numbers because we did not like the fact that the space of rational numbers was not complete. We can now show that, with our definition, we have achieved our goal.

If $\mathfrak{C} \in \alpha$ is a C-filter in Q, then $\lim \bar{\mathfrak{C}} = \alpha$ in R.

---

[1] Q^{+} is the set of positive rational numbers.
[2] In order to define the neighbourhood of a point of R one can proceed differently. One can limit oneself to intervals of the type $]\alpha - \frac{1}{n}, \alpha + \frac{1}{n}[$ or one can also allow unsymmetric intervals $]\alpha - \bar{p}, \alpha + \bar{q}[$. The filters given by the different sets of intervals are equivalent, and it is a question of convention which one calls the 'neighbourhood filter'.

Here $\bar{\mathfrak{C}}$ is the set of all *real* numbers, that can be obtained from the elements of $\mathfrak{C}$ by the correspondence $q \to \bar{q}$ ($q \in Q$). To prove the theorem we have to show that

$$\bar{\mathfrak{C}} \lhd \mathfrak{U}(\alpha) \qquad (30)$$

More explicitly this means that for every interval $]\alpha - \bar{q}, \alpha + \bar{q}[$ ($q \in Q$) there exists a set $\bar{C} \in \bar{\mathfrak{C}}$ which is contained in the interval.

Let us begin with an arbitrary $\frac{q}{2}$-set $C \in \mathfrak{C}$. Then

$$|c - c'| < \frac{q}{2} \qquad (31)$$

for all $c, c' \in C$. Then

$$\mathfrak{C}' = \{C'/C' \subset C \wedge C' \in \mathfrak{C}\}$$

is a filter which is equivalent to $\mathfrak{C}$.[1] We have $\mathfrak{C} \sim \mathfrak{C}'$ and, *a fortiori*, $\mathfrak{C} \approx \mathfrak{C}'$, *i.e.*, $\mathfrak{C}' \in \alpha$. By (31) the C-filters

$$\{\{c\}\} - \mathfrak{C}' + \{\{q\}\} \qquad (32)$$

and

$$\mathfrak{C}' - \{\{c\}\} + \{\{q\}\} \qquad (32')$$

have the lower bound $\frac{q}{2}$. Their sets are sets of positive rational numbers. Hence the real numbers represented by them lie in R^+. We thus have

$$[\{\{c\}\} - \mathfrak{C}' + \{\{q\}\}] = \bar{c} - \alpha + \bar{q} \in R^+$$
$$[\mathfrak{C}' - \{\{c\}\} + \{\{q\}\}] = \alpha - \bar{c} + \bar{q} \in R^+$$

for all $c \in C$, so that $\bar{c} \in \bar{C}$. This means that

$$\bar{c} > \alpha - \bar{q}, \qquad \alpha + \bar{q} > \bar{c}$$

and hence

$$\bar{c} \in]\alpha - \bar{q}, \alpha + \bar{q}[$$

so that (30) is proved.

We have thus shown that the real numbers defined in VIII 1 do indeed possess the desired properties. To every C-filter $\mathfrak{C}$ on Q belongs a limit in R. If $\mathfrak{C}$ converges to a rational number q, then

---

[1]Cf. the method of proof of the auxiliary theorem of VIII 2.

we have the case symbolized in Fig. 40a. All filters equivalent to $\mathfrak{C}$ converge to q. However, if there exists no limit in Q for such a class of filters $[\mathfrak{C}]$, then the filters $\bar{\mathfrak{C}}$ of real numbers corresponding to the filters $\mathfrak{C}$ converge to the real number β which is defined by $[\mathfrak{C}]$. Thus we can now insert the real number β in the open disc of Fig. 40b.

We may now conclude our general considerations of real numbers by the fundamental theorem on completeness:

(A) *The space R of real numbers is complete.*

This theorem (A) is *not yet proved*. We have shown only that to every C-filter $\mathfrak{C}$ of rational numbers there belongs a corresponding C-filter $\bar{\mathfrak{C}}$, which converges to a real number β, determined by this filter. Beyond this, theorem (A) asserts that *all* C-filters on R converge to a real number.

We shall obtain the proof of (A) as a consequence of further theorems which are of interest in themselves, and not only because they form the elements of the proof of (A).

(B) *R is a smallest extension field of Q in which all C-filters of Q converge.*[1]

This is an immediate consequence of our latest arguments. Let T be a proper subspace of R and $\alpha \in R$, $\alpha \notin T$. Then none of the C-filters $\mathfrak{C}$ from α converges in the subspace T, since $\lim \mathfrak{C} = \alpha$.

Thus one may not remove any element from R without disturbing the completeness. On the other hand it is also not possible to extend the space R, maintaining its ordering properties:

(C) *R is a maximal archimedean ordered*[2] *extension field of Q.*
    More explicitly:

(C') *Every archimedean ordered extension field S of Q which contains R is identical with R.*

We first define in S, by a set of intervals, the neighbourhood filter $\mathfrak{U}(s)$.

$$\mathfrak{U}(s) = \{]s-q, s+q[\} = \{\{t/t \in S \wedge s-q < t < s+q\}\},$$
$$s \in S, q \in Q \tag{33}$$

---

[1] Here, and in the sequel, we identify Q with $\bar{Q}$, q with $\bar{q}$ etc.

[2] A space is said to be archimedean ordered if for its elements the ordering laws of Q (see III 7) are satisfied: in particular, to every element s of such an extension space S there must exist a natural number n with the property $n > s$.

We now assume that R is a *proper* part of S. Let s, for example, be an element of S that does not belong to R:

$$s \in S, \qquad s \notin R \tag{34}$$

We shall show that the assumption (34) is false, and we first prove that the extension space S with the interval topology (33) is, in any case, *separable*.

Let s and t be elements of S with $s > t$ and m a natural number which satisfies the inequality

$$m > \frac{1}{s-t} \tag{35}$$

Since S is assumed to be archimedean ordered, such a number m must exist. From (35), $s - t > m^{-1}$, and it follows that

$$\left(s - \frac{1}{n}\right) - \left(t + \frac{1}{n}\right) = (s-t) - \frac{2}{n} > \frac{1}{m} - \frac{2}{n}$$

But

$$\frac{1}{m} - \frac{2}{n} > 0 \quad \text{if} \quad n > 2m$$

Therefore in this case the intervals

$$\left]t - \frac{1}{n}, t + \frac{1}{n}\right[; \qquad \left]s - \frac{1}{n}, s + \frac{1}{n}\right[$$

are disjoint. The topology in S is thus separable.

Now the next step in our proof is to show that each interval

$$U_n(s) = \left]s - \frac{1}{n}, s + \frac{1}{n}\right[\qquad (s \in S)$$

contains *rational numbers*. Because of the archimedean ordering of the elements of S there exists a natural number m such that $-m < s < +m$. If m itself (or $-m$) already lies in $U_n(s)$, then our proof is complete, since m is rational. But if neither m nor $-m$ belongs to the interval, then we have

$$-m < s - \frac{1}{n} < s + \frac{1}{n} < +m$$

We now consider the rational numbers p/q with a fixed denominator $q > n$, which lie between $-m$ and $+m$. There are a finite number of them and hence there will be a greatest number p_1/q (in the set of all numbers p/q) which satisfies the inequality

$$\frac{p_1}{q} < s - \frac{1}{n}$$

and a smallest for which

$$\frac{p_2}{q} > s + \frac{1}{n}$$

Since

$$\frac{p_2}{q} - \frac{p_1}{q} > \frac{2}{n} > \frac{1}{q}$$

at least one further number p^*/q lies between p_1/q and p_2/q. This number is then contained in $U_n(s)$: $p^*/q \in U_n(s)$. Hence the intersection

$$\left] s - \frac{1}{n}, s + \frac{1}{n} \right[\cap Q \tag{36}$$

is not empty. The sets (36) (for $n = 1, 2, 3, \ldots$) thus form a filter $\mathfrak{C}$ which is clearly finer than the neighbourhood filter $\mathfrak{U}(s)$: $\mathfrak{C} \lhd \mathfrak{U}(s)$. We have therefore

$$\lim \mathfrak{C} = s \tag{37}$$

in the space S. We now note that the filter (36) contains only sets whose elements are *rational numbers*. The C-filter (36) therefore converges to a real number α. Since S is separable with respect to the interval topology, each convergent filter in S cannot possess more than one limit, by the general theorem of VII 5. Hence, by (37), we have $\alpha = s$ and thus $s \in R$. The assumption (35) was false; there exists no element of S which does not also belong to R.

After these preparatory remarks the proof of (A) is simple. Let us suppose that there exist C-filters of real numbers which do not converge to elements of R. We could then construct a field S whose elements are the classes of C-equivalent filters in R. By a method similar to the construction of R from Q, one can show that S has all the properties of a field, and by introducing an interval topology it can be made into a topological space.

S contains, of course, the numbers $[\{\{\alpha\}\}]$ with $\alpha \in R$, but also elements of the type $\bar{\bar{q}} = [\{\{\bar{q}\}\}]$, $q \in Q$. These elements too form a subfield of S. Now S can be archimedean ordered, just as R can.

It is an extension field[1] of Q, as has just been remarked. Hence, by theorem (C), S is identical with R. On the other hand, every C-filter from R converges in S to an element of S. This can be shown in the same way as the corresponding statement for the fields R and Q (see p. 172). Hence we have shown:

Every C-filter in R converges to an element of R. R is indeed complete.

In proving theorem (C) we have obtained a result which merits special emphasis:

(D) *The points of the space Q are everywhere dense in R.*

Expressed differently:

(D′) *Every point of R is a point of accumulation of Q.*

A point p of a space P is called a *point of accumulation* of a set M, if every neighbourhood of p contains (at least) one point of M. As shown on p. 174, in every interval

$$\left]\alpha - \frac{1}{n}, \alpha + \frac{1}{n}\right[\qquad (\alpha \in R)$$

there lies (at least) one rational number.

5. Representation of real numbers

We have defined the real number as a class of filters, that is to say as a set whose elements are sets of sets. It is not easy to visualise such 'numbers'. One is helped in this by selecting from the class of filters of the number $\alpha = [\mathfrak{C}]$ a particularly simple filter $\mathfrak{C}^*$ for the 'representation' of the number. For this purpose the 'decimal fraction filter'[2] suggests itself, of which an example has already been given in VIII 1.

We recall the well known representation of a rational number by a periodic decimal fraction. The equation

$$\tfrac{1}{3} = 0 \cdot 333\bar{3} \ldots \tag{38}$$

can be interpreted as follows: The set of intervals

$$\{\ldots]0 \cdot 333 \ldots 33, 0 \cdot 333 \ldots 34[\ldots\}$$

---

[1] Here we identify q with $\bar{q}$ and $\bar{\bar{q}}$, Q with $\bar{Q}$ and the subfield $\bar{\bar{Q}}$ of S.
[2] Abbreviated to 'decimal filter'.

forms a filter $\mathfrak{F}(\frac{1}{3})$, which converges to the rational number $\frac{1}{3}$. For

$$\frac{1}{3} = [\mathfrak{F}(\tfrac{1}{3})]$$

we write more simply (38). In general

$$\alpha = a \cdot a_1 a_2 a_3 \ldots a_n a_{n+1} \ldots$$

stands for

$$\alpha = \left[\{\ldots]a \cdot a_1 a_2 a_3 \ldots a_n a_{n+1}, a \cdot a_1 a_2 a_3 \ldots a_n (a_{n+1}+1)[\ldots\}\right]$$

In VIII 1 we have already shown how a decimal filter can be obtained for the real number α, whose square is equal to 2. Now the question arises as to how to find the decimal fraction expansion of a real number which is given by any one of its C-filters. Take, as an example, the remainder filter $\mathfrak{F}$ defined in (2) for the sequence (1). By (2'), for $n > 1$ and all natural numbers m, we have

$$|e_n - e_{n+m}| < \frac{2}{(n+1)!} \tag{39}$$

It is known that the sequence $a^n/n!$ converges (even for $a > 1$) to 0. Hence for sufficiently large n[1]

$$\frac{2}{(n+1)!} < 10^{-n-1}$$

From (39) it therefore follows that

$$|e_n - e_{n+m}| < 10^{-n-1} \tag{40}$$

for $n > 26$. Now let

$$e_n = 2 \cdot a_1 a_2 a_3 \ldots a_n a_{n+1} \ldots$$

be the decimal expansion of the rational number e_n. By (40) the elements of the set

$$\{e_{n+1}, e_{n+2}, e_{n+3}, \ldots\}$$

lie in the interval

$$]2 \cdot a_1 a_2 \ldots a_n, 2 \cdot a_1 a_2 \ldots a_{n-1}(a_n+1)[\tag{41}$$

Assume that the digit a_n is different from 9. Then $2 \cdot a_1 a_2 \ldots a_n$ is the beginning of the decimal expansion of the real number $[\mathfrak{F}]$ (up to the n-th digit). If $a_n = 9$, then one considers the expansion

---

[1] It is sufficient to take $n > 26$.

for a number $n' > n$. In this way one obtains[1] for the real number e[2] given by the filter (2) the decimal expansion

$$e = 2{\cdot}7182818284\ldots \qquad (42)$$

It is neither finite nor periodic, since e is not rational (see VIII 1).

For numbers given by other filters, the appropriate decimal expansion can, in general, be obtained by simple calculation. There are, however, cases in which the actual calculation of the decimal fraction is *not* possible. We shall show this by an example.

The calculation of the decimal fraction (42) for the number e can be carried arbitrarily far by means of modern calculating machines. Now it could happen that among the digits of e the 10 digits occur in their natural order:

$$e = 2{\cdot}7182818284\ldots 0123456789\ldots$$

So far this has not happened, as far as calculations have been made, but such a possibility is conceivable. It is also possible that some day a proof will be found that such a sequence of digits in the expansion of e is *not possible*. We now define a number theoretical function[3] as follows:

$$E(n) = \begin{cases} 1, \text{ if among the digits of the decimal (42)} \\ \quad \textit{no} \text{ sequence 0123456789 occurs up to} \\ \quad \text{the } n\text{-th digit,} \\ 0, \text{ otherwise} \end{cases} \qquad (43)$$

The function $E(n)$ defined by (43) can obviously be determined for all natural numbers n. One has only to carry out the expansion of the decimal (42) to the n-th place to obtain $E(n)$. For all numbers n considered so far, $E(n) = 1$. If there exists a smallest number n for which $E(n) = 0$, we shall denote it by N. We should then have

$$, E(N-1) = 1, E(N) = 0, E(N+1) = 0, \ldots \qquad (44)$$

---

[1] The reader should consider why it is impossible that $a_{n'} = 9$ for *all* numbers $n' > n$.

[2] This number, investigated by Euler, is usually introduced as the limit of the number sequence

$$\left\{ \left(1 + \frac{1}{n} \right)^{n} \right\}$$

See problems 1 and 2 of this chapter.

[3] A number theoretical function $f(n)$ is a function which assigns to the natural number n, the natural number $f(n)$.

We now define a number sequence $a(n)$ by

$$a(n) = 1 + (-1)^n \cdot 10^{-n} \cdot E(n) + (-1)^N \cdot 10^{-N} \cdot (1 - E(n)) \quad (45)$$

When $n < N$, then $a(n) = 1 + (-1)^n 10^{-n}$, since for these numbers $E(n) = 1$, $1 - E(n) = 0$. On the other hand, $a(n) = 1 + (-1)^N 10^{-N}$ for all $n \geqslant N$. The filter of the remainders

$$\{\ldots \{a(n+1), a(n+2), a(n+3), \ldots\} \ldots\} \quad (46)$$

is clearly a C-filter, since for all n and m we have $|a(n) - a(n+m)| < 2 \cdot 10^{-n}$.

It is clear that the filter (46) converges to 1, if there is *no* sequence of digits 0123456789 in the decimal expansion of e. It converges to the rational number $1 + (-1)^N \cdot 10^{-N}$ if such a digit sequence *does* exist.

Thus we have a real number γ, defined by the filter (46), (or by the sequence (45)), for which we cannot give a decimal expansion so long as the problem of the digit sequence remains undecided. For we have $\gamma = 1$ if no such sequence exists, $\gamma < 1$ if N is odd and $\gamma > 1$ if N is even. It is, of course, possible to calculate γ to any degree of accuracy, but nevertheless one cannot say whether a decimal expansion of γ begins with 0·... or with 1·....

Should the reader succeed in solving this 'decision problem', then the sequence (45) would have lost its interest. However, since there are still many unsolved number theoretical problems, it is not difficult to create further examples of real numbers that cannot be calculated.[1]

The example just given brings out the difficulties that may occur in the calculation of the decimal expansion of a real number. We begin with the fact that each C-filter contains ε-sets for arbitrary small ε. Thus, in particular, each filter contains 10^{-n-1}-sets for every natural number n. Hence one can easily find a filter C' which is C-equivalent to $C \in \alpha$, and whose sets are all contained in an interval of length 10^{-n-1}. This suggests the idea of including this set in an interval of the type

$$]a \cdot a_1 a_2 a_3 \ldots a_n, a \cdot a_1 a_2 a_3 \ldots (a_n + 1)[\quad (47)$$

However, this is not always possible. Even if the sets of the filter belong to an interval whose length is only $\frac{1}{10}$ (or $\frac{1}{100} \ldots$) of the length of the interval (47), the inclusion in an interval of type (47) can be impossible. For example, the 10^{-n-1}-interval may contain

---

[1]For 'decision problems', see, for example, Chapter XI of Meschkowski (2).

the left hand end point of (47) as an interior point. If this is the case for all 10^{-n-1}-sets of the filter (for arbitrarily large n), then the problem of decimal representation is solved: our filter then converges to the rational number $a \cdot a_1 a_2 a_3 \ldots a_n$.

However, if the filter sets cannot be enclosed in the desired manner, *and* if it cannot be decided whether any one of the end points of the interval sets (47) is the limit of the filter, then the calculation of the decimal fraction that corresponds to the filter is not possible.

Nevertheless, for the practically important cases, the calculation of the decimal fraction expansion can generally be carried out without difficulty.

When using modern calculating machines, the representation of real numbers in the *binary system* is useful:

$$\alpha = b^{(n)} \cdot 2^n + b^{(n-1)} \cdot 2^{n-1} + \ldots + b^{(0)} \cdot 2^0 + \frac{b_1}{2} + \frac{b_2}{2^2} + \frac{b_3}{2^3} + \ldots \quad (48)$$

Here the numbers b_v and $b^{(v)}$ are equal to 0 or 1. To distinguish them from the digits of the decimal system one can use the symbols $\circ$ and $|$ instead of 0 and 1 and write, for example, $||.\circ|$ for

$$3\tfrac{1}{4} = 1 \cdot 2' + 1 \cdot 2^0 + 0 \cdot 2^{-1} + 1 \cdot 2^{-2}$$

The series expansion (48) replaces the somewhat clumsy representation of real numbers by 'binary filters' which have the form

$$\alpha = [\{\ldots\} b \cdot b_1 b_2 \ldots b_n, b \cdot b_1 b_2 \ldots (b_n+1)[\ldots\}]$$
$$b = b^{(n)} \cdot 2^n + b^{(n-1)} \cdot 2^{n-1} + \ldots + b^{(0)} \cdot 2^0 \quad (48')$$

The problems that occur in calculations with real numbers when binary filters are used are the same as those encountered with decimal fractions.

A representation by a finite decimal fraction is possible only for rational numbers p/q having a denominator q of the form $q = 2^n \cdot 5^m$. Finite binary fractions are obtained for numbers p/q if, and only if, $q = 2^n$. There exists, however, a representation by series (or by the corresponding remainder filter) by which an expansion in a *finite* series is possible for *all* rational numbers (and only for these). We refer to the representation of a number by the Cantor series

$$\gamma = c_1 + \frac{c_2}{2!} + \frac{c_3}{3!} + \ldots + \frac{c_n}{n!} + \ldots \quad (49)$$

The coefficients c_n can be chosen in such a way that $0 \leqslant c_n < n$.[1]

6. Problems

1. Let $\mathfrak{F}$ be the filter defined by (2) and $\mathfrak{G}$ the remainder filter of the sequence $\left\{\left(1+\dfrac{1}{n}\right)^n\right\}$. Show that they are C-equivalent.

2. Let $\mathfrak{F}_1$ be the decimal filter of the real number e, given by the intervals (41), $\mathfrak{F}_2$ the filter of the intervals

$$\left]\left(1+\frac{1}{n}\right)^n, \left(1+\frac{1}{n}\right)^{n+1}\right[,$$

$\mathfrak{F}_3$, $\mathfrak{F}_4$ the remainder filters of the sequences

$$\left\{\left(1+\frac{1}{n}\right)^{2n}\right\}, \left\{\left(1-\frac{1}{n}\right)^n\right\}$$

respectively.

   a) Which of the filters $\mathfrak{F}$, $\mathfrak{G}$ (problem 1), $\mathfrak{F}_2$, $\mathfrak{F}_3$, $\mathfrak{F}_4$ are equivalent and which are C-equivalent?
   b) Which real numbers are determined by the filters mentioned in a)?

3. Show that between any two real numbers there is always a rational number.

4. Write $\frac{2}{3}$ as a binary fraction.

---

[1]One can find further information about these and other series expansions in Perron. Cf. also § I, 5 of Meschkowski (6).

Solutions to Problems

II. Sets

1. If one sets up the truth table (analogously to (10)) for the truth values of the two propositions $\neg(A \wedge B)$ and $(\neg A) \vee (\neg B)$, one obtains (for all possible combinations of the truth values of A and B) the same truth values for the propositions on the left and on the right of the symbol $\Leftrightarrow$. (36) is justified in a similar way.

2. The two propositions connected by $\Leftrightarrow$ in (37) are true if, and only if, $A \cap B = \varnothing$.

3. $B = \varnothing$, $A = \varnothing$.

4. If $x \in A \cap C$, then x belongs to the left hand, but not to the right hand set.

5. $(x \in A) \wedge [\neg (x \in A - B)] \Leftrightarrow (x \in A) \wedge [\neg \{(x \in A) \wedge (x \notin B)\}]$
   $\qquad\qquad\qquad\qquad \Leftrightarrow (x \in A) \wedge [(x \notin A) \vee (x \in B)]$
   $\qquad\qquad\qquad\qquad \Leftrightarrow [(x \in A) \wedge (x \notin A)] \vee [(x \in A) \wedge (x \in B)].$

   Since the proposition $(x \in A) \wedge (x \notin A)$ is certainly false, the original proposition is true if, and only if,

$$(x \in A) \wedge (x \in B)$$

   is true; but this is what we had to prove.

6. Let K be a semi-circle of diameter $\overline{AB}$ with centre M, which touches the line $\overline{AB}$ at its mid point C; $\overline{CM} \perp \overline{AB}$ (see Fig. 41).

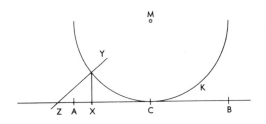

FIG. 41.

By parallel projection, perpendicular to $\overline{AB}$, every point $X \in \overline{AB}$ is mapped on to a point Y of the semi-circle. A central projection with centre M then maps the point Y on to the point Z of the line AB. This mapping $X \leftrightarrow Y \leftrightarrow Z$ is clearly one-to-one.

7. $h = n + \sum\limits_{v=0}^{n} |a_v|$ is called the 'height' of the polynomial (40) which belongs to a given algebraic number. To every natural number h there obviously belong only a finite number of polynomials, and to each polynomial (40) n zeros. Hence one can enumerate all algebraic numbers according to increasing heights.

III. Rational numbers

1. By (3'), $(a+b)+1 = (a+b)' = a+b' = a+(b+1)$. Thus (5) is true for $c = 1$. Suppose that (5) is true for $c = k$:

$$(a+b)+k = a+(b+k).$$

Then

$$(a+b)+(k+1) = (a+b)+k' = ((a+b)+k)'$$

$$= (a+(b+k))' = a+(b+k)'$$

$$= a+((b+k)+1) = a+(b+(k+1)).$$

Hence (5) is true for all natural numbers c.

2. $2.1 = 2$,
$2.2 = 2.1' = 2.1+2 = 2+2 = 0''+0'' = 4$.

3. Take the proof of (5) in 1 as a pattern.

4. The proof is by the method of mathematical induction. The theorem is true for $n = 1$. It is assumed true for $n = k$. Then, by the binomial theorem,

$$(k+1)^p - (k+1) = k^p + \binom{p}{1}k^{p-1} + \ldots + 1 - k - 1$$

$$= (k^p - k) + \left[\binom{p}{1}k^{p-1} + \binom{p}{2}k^{p-2} + \ldots + \binom{p}{p-1}k \right].$$

Both brackets are divisible by p. The first is, by the induction hypothesis. In the second the binomial coefficients $\binom{p}{v}$ are *integers*.

Since p is a prime number, the factor p in the numerator of $\binom{p}{v}$ certainly does not cancel. Since every term in the second bracket is divisible by p, their sum must also be. Thus we have shown that $(k+1)^p - (k+1)$ is divisible by p. Hence Fermat's theorem is true for all natural numbers.

5. This theorem can also be proved by mathematical induction. But it is more simply proved as follows:

$$f(n) = n^3 - n = n(n^2 - 1) = (n-1) \cdot n \cdot (n+1)$$

Thus $f(n)$ is the product of three consecutive natural numbers. Exactly one of them is divisible by 3, at least one is divisible by 2. Hence $f(n)$ is divisible by $2 \cdot 3 = 6$.

6. No. The subset with the property $x > 0$, for example, has no smallest element.

7. Every natural number $n > b \cdot c \geq \dfrac{b \cdot c}{a \cdot d}$ has the required property.

8. $n \cdot (0, 1) = (0, n) \prec (1, 0)$ for all natural numbers n.

IV. Groups

1. Hint: Show that

$$(p + iq)(r + is) = p' + iq'$$
$$(p + iq)^{-1} = r' + is'$$

for suitable rational numbers p', q', r', s'. The proof of the remaining group properties is trivial.

2. The method of proof is similar to that of problem 1.

3. By a suitable numbering of the permutations one obtains the group G_{10}, isomorphic to the group G_3.

4. Let $g_1 = e$, $\qquad g_2 = (1\ 2\ 3\ 4)$, $\qquad g_3 = g_2^2$, $\qquad g_4 = g_2^3$,

$$g_5 = \begin{pmatrix} 1 & 2 & 3 & 4 \\ 1 & 4 & 3 & 2 \end{pmatrix}, \qquad g_6 = g_5 \circ g_2, \qquad g_7 = g_5 \circ g_3,$$

$g_8 = g_5 \circ g_4$.

The table of this group G_{12} is then as follows:

Group table for G_{12}

	1	2	3	4	5	6	7	8
1	1	2	3	4	5	6	7	8
2	2	3	4	1	8	5	6	7
3	3	4	1	2	7	8	5	6
4	4	1	2	3	6	7	8	5
5	5	6	7	8	1	2	3	4
6	6	7	8	5	4	1	2	3
7	7	8	5	6	3	4	1	2
8	8	5	6	7	2	3	4	1

5. One can bring each of the 8 corners into the position 1, and then rotate the cube about the diagonal through 1 through 0°, 120° or 240°. This gives altogether $8 . 3 = 24$ possibilities. Thus the permutation group belonging to the cube consists of 24 permutations of order 8.

6. Similarly the octahedron group contains 24 permutations; they are of order 6. Since one can inscribe an octahedron in a cube in such a way that the vertices of the octahedron are the mid points of the faces of the cube, every rotation or reflection of the cube also brings the octahedron into coincidence with itself, and vice versa. Consequently the two groups are isomorphic.

7. $G_{13} = Z \cup (Z+i) \cup (Z-i) \cup (Z+2i) \cup \ldots$

8. G_{14}, as a group of prime order, has only itself and the group $\{e\}$ consisting of the identity element e as subgroups. This follows from the theorem proved on p. 92.

V. Rings and fields

1. Define a cyclic ordering in M_5 as in Fig. 42.

Thus, for example, $|$ is the successor of $\circ$, $\uparrow$ the successor of $|$, ...,

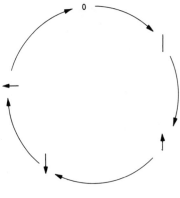

FIG. 42.

∘ succeeds ←. If we again denote the successor of m by m', then we can define addition and multiplication as follows:

$$m + \circ = m, \quad m \cdot | = m, \quad m + | = m',$$
$$mn' = mn + m, \quad m + n' = (m+n)'$$

2. This follows from the congruences:

$$10^v \equiv 1 \ (\mathrm{mod}\ 9), \qquad 10^v \equiv (-1)^v \ (\mathrm{mod}\ 11).$$

3. Let $a \cdot b = o$, $a \neq o$. By (4), $a \cdot o = o$. Thus we have $a \cdot b = a \cdot o$. From the property a) of the integral domain it then follows that $b = o$.

4. a) The set of even numbers: it contains no identity element.
   b) The set of integers.

5. The dual numbers form a ring, but since $\varepsilon^2 = 0$, they do not form an integral domain.

6. The formula is proved as in elementary algebra from the rules for an integral domain.

7. No. The distributive law is not always satisfied. For example

$$\uparrow \cdot (\uparrow + \downarrow) = \uparrow \cdot | = \uparrow$$
$$\uparrow \cdot \uparrow + \uparrow \cdot \downarrow = \downarrow + | = \circ$$

VI. Lattices

1. See Fig. 43.

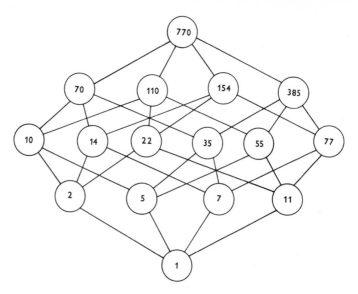

FIG. 43.

2. Using (9) and noting the lattice axioms one obtains:

$$(a \sqcup b) \sqcap (a \sqcup c = [(a \sqcup b) \sqcap a] \sqcup [(a \sqcup b) \sqcap c]$$
$$= a \sqcup [(a \sqcup b) \sqcap c] = a \sqcup [(a \sqcap c) \sqcup (b \sqcap c)]$$
$$= [a \sqcup (a \sqcap c)] \sqcup (b \sqcap c) = a \sqcup (b \sqcap c)$$

3. a and c.
4. See Fig. 44.

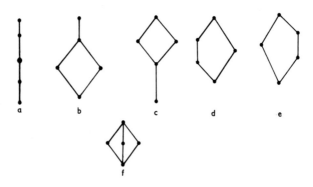

FIG. 44.

5. a) No. b) $z = x+iy \sqcup Z = X+iY$, if $x < X$.
6. a, c, d.
7. It is not. Counter example: Let q and r be lines of a plane α, and let p be a line skew to both of them. Then

$$p \sqcap (q \sqcup r) = p \sqcap \alpha = Q$$

where Q is the point in which p meets the plane α.
On the other hand

$$(p \sqcap q) \sqcup (p \sqcap r) = \phi \sqcup \phi = \phi$$

VII. Spaces

1. The series for $D(x, y)$ is majorized by the convergent series $\sum n^{-2}$. Thus it is itself convergent. The validity of the axioms for a metric space is established as in Example (D) of VII 1.
2. There exist neighbourhoods of 0, 1 (for example $]-\frac{1}{2}, +\frac{1}{2}[,]\frac{1}{2}, \frac{3}{2}[)$ which do not contain $1, 0$ respectively. Hence the remainder filter is not finer than the neighbourhood filter of 0 or 1 (or any other number).
3. An infinite series with partial sums

$$s_n = u_1 + u_2 + u_3 + \ldots + u_n$$

is said to be convergent if the filter

$$\{\{s_{n+1}, s_{n+2}, s_{n+3}, \ldots\}\}$$

is a C-filter.
4. $a, b, d, e; a$.
5. None.
6. $\mathfrak{F}_1 \lhd \mathfrak{F}_2, \mathfrak{F}_2 \lhd \mathfrak{F}_1, \mathfrak{F}_3 \lhd \mathfrak{F}_1, \mathfrak{F}_3 \lhd \mathfrak{F}_2$.
7. $\mathfrak{F}_1 \sim \mathfrak{F}_2, \mathfrak{F}_1 \approx \mathfrak{F}_2 \approx \mathfrak{F}_3$.

VIII. Real numbers

1. By the binomial theorem

$$e_n^* = \left(1 + \frac{1}{n}\right)^n$$

$$= 1 + 1 + \frac{1}{2!}\left(1 - \frac{1}{n}\right) + \ldots + \frac{1}{n!}\left(1 - \frac{1}{n}\right)\left(1 - \frac{2}{n}\right)\ldots\left(1 - \frac{n-1}{n}\right)$$

It follows from this that

$$|e_n - e_n^*| < \frac{1}{n}$$

Using the inequality (2') as well, one can easily show that $\mathfrak{F} \sqcup \mathfrak{G}$ is a C-filter.

2. a) $\mathfrak{F} \approx \mathfrak{G} \approx \mathfrak{F}_1 \approx \mathfrak{F}_2 \,;\, \mathfrak{F}_1 \sim \mathfrak{F}_2.$

   b) $[\mathfrak{F}] = [\mathfrak{G}] = [\mathfrak{F}_1] = [\mathfrak{F}_2] = e,\, [\mathfrak{F}_3] = e^2,\, [\mathfrak{F}_4] = \dfrac{1}{e}.$

3. This is a consequence of Theorem (D).

4. $\frac{2}{3} = \circ.|\circ|\circ|\circ\ldots.$

Bibliography

ALEXANDROFF, P. S.: *Einführung in die Mengenlehre und die Theorie der reellen Funktionen.* Berlin 1956.

BLASCHKE, W.: *Projektive Geometrie.* Wolfenbüttel-Hannover 1948.

BONOLA, R.: *Noneuclidean Geometry.* New York. Dover. 1955.

BOURBAKI, N.: *Toyologie générale.* Paris 1951. Chapters I, II, III, IV, IX.

DEDEKIND, R.: *Was sind und was sollen die Zahlen?* 8 Aufl. Brunswick 1960.

ERWE, F.: *Differential- und Integralrechnung I und II.* B.I-Hochschultaschenbücher 30/30a, 31/31a. Mannheim 1962.

FELIX, L.: *Exposé moderne des mathematiques élémentaires.* Paris 1959.

FRAENKEL, A.: *Einleitung in die Mengenlehre.* Berlin 1925.

GERICKE, H.: *Lattice Theory.* Harrap 1966.

GOODSTEIN, R. L.: (1) *Constructive Formalism.* Leicester 1951.

GOODSTEIN, R. L.: (2) *Fundamental Concepts of Mathematics.* Pergamon 1962.

HAHN, ELLERS and DZEWAS: *Eine Einführung in die Analysis mittels des Filterbegriffs.* MNU 13, 1960/114, 1961 (8 and 10).

HAUPT, O.: *Einführung in die Algebra I.* Leipzig 1952.

HERMES, H.: *Einführung in die Verbandstheorie.* Berlin-Gottingen-Heidelberg 1955.

HILBERT, D.: (1) *The Foundations of Geometry.* Open Court Publ. Co. 1902.

HILBERT, D.: (2) *Gesammelte Abhandlungen.* Berlin 1935.

HILBERT, D. and ACKERMANN, W.: *Grundzüge der theoretischen Logik.* Berlin-Göttingen-Heidelberg 1949.

HILBERT, D. and FREGE, G.: *Briefwechsel.* Published by G. Steck. Sitzungsber. Heidelberger Ak. d. Wiss. (math.-nat. Kl. Jahrgang 1941).

KAMKE, E.: *Theory of Sets.* New York. Dover publications. 1950.

KEMENY, J. G., SNELL, J. L. and THOMPSON, G. L.: *Introduction to Finite Mathematics.* Prentice-Hall, Englewood Cliffs, N.J. 1957.

KLEENE, S. C.: *Introduction to Metamathematics.* Amsterdam-Groningen 1952.

KUROSCH, A. G.: *Theory of Groups.* Chelsea Publ. Co. New York 1955.

LANDAU, E.: *Foundations of Analysis.* Chelsea Publ. Co. New York 1960.

LENZ, H.: *Grundlagen der Elementarmathematik.* Berlin 1961.

LORENZEN, P.: (1) *Einführung in die operative Logik und Mathematik.* Berlin-Göttingen-Heidelberg 1955.

LORENZEN, P.: (2) *Metamathematik.* B.I-Hochschultaschenbücher 25, Mannheim 1962.

MARCH, A.: *Der Weg des Universums.* Bern 1948.

MESCHKOWSKI, H.: (1) *Noneuclidean Geometry*. Academic Press. New York 1964.

MESCHKOWSKI, H.: (2) *Wandlungen des mathematischen Denkens*. 2 Aufl. Brunswick 1960.

MESCHKOWSKI, H.: (3) *Unsolved and Unsolvable Problems in Geometry*. Oliver and Boyd 1966.

MESCHKOWSKI, H.: (4) *Das Christentum im Jahrhundert der Naturwissenschaften*. Munich 1961.

MESCHKOWSKI, H.: (5) *Denkweisen grosser Mathematiker*. Brunswick 1961.

MESCHKOWSKI, H.: (6) *Unendliche Reihen*. B.I-Hochschultaschenbücher 35, Mannheim 1962.

MESCHKOWSKI, H.: (7) *Reihenentwicklungen in der mathematischen Physik*. B.I-Hochschultaschenbücher 51, Mannheim 1963.

OEEC: *New Thinking in School Mathematics*. Paris 1961.

PERRON, O.: *Irrationalzahlen*. Berlin 1947.

PESCHL, E.: *Analytische Geometrie*. B.I-Hochschultaschenbücher 15/15a. Mannheim 1961.

ROSENBLOOM, R.: *The Elements of Mathematical Logic*. New York 1950.

SIERPINSKI, W.: *Algèbre des ensembles*. Warsaw 1951.

STEGMÜLLER, W.: *Metaphysik-Wissenschaft-Skepsis*. Frankfurt-Wien 1954.

VOGEL, A.: *Klassiche Grundlagen der Analysis*. Leipzig 1952.

WEYL, H.: *Symmetry*. Princeton 1952.

Index